The Law of Longer Life

THE LAW OF LONGER LIFE

By

C. Northcote Parkinson

and

Herman Le Compte

TROY STATE UNIVERSITY PRESS
TROY, ALABAMA

Published in German as
Wir Kinder des Methusalem, 1978
by Econ Verlagsgruppe

CONTENTS

PREFACE

The problem of how to enjoy a longer effective life is of such importance that a book on the subject cannot well be ignored. It is the more essential, therefore, that the authors should not claim too much. We should be rash to pretend that we have solved overnight a problem which has baffled mankind since the dawn of history. We should be prepared to maintain that we have made a contribution to the subject, but we do not forget that other people are working in the same field and that other research programmes are likely to produce other results. Any gerontologist may be tempted to claim that people who avoid certain bad habits, who take regular exercise and adhere to a certain diet, swallowing the tablets as prescribed, will live to the age of a hundred. But his potential patients must realise at once that his claim is not easy to prove. If a person aged sixty is told that a certain treatment will enable him to live to the age of ninety, it will take thirty years to discover whether the treatment is effective. A geriatric specialist may point to a patient aged eighty and can describe his treatment over the last twenty years. But this proves nothing. We see the patient who has survived, but not the other nineteen who are already dead. Nor do we know that the patient would not have lived to eighty without any treatment at all. We have to conclude, therefore, that this is a field of research in which no quick results are possible. Whatever claim we put forward must take a lifetime to substantiate.

It could be argued, however, that some facts about longevity have been ascertained in certain parts of the world where people are known to live to a great age. There is Ecuador, for example, where there are records of people living to the age of 150. In remote villages such as Vilcabamba in the Andes, people still work at the age of 100. Theirs is a diet based on fresh fruit and vegetables, lean meat, little fat, unstrained honey and rum. Inhabitants of the Caucasus have included one who died in 1973, aged 168. On his birthday in 1972, he is said to have performed a local dance with two of his grandsons aged respectively 88 and 71. A woman in the same region lived to over 160. We hear of a short distance race on foot with competitors aged from 80 to 104. The man who had won the race the previous year (aged 93) could not compete because he was on his honeymoon. Again, we hear of a diet based on green vegetables, lean meat, fruit juice and fruit — this time with milk as well — plus alcohol. Then there is the valley of Hunza in the Himalayas isolated for 2,000 years, it is said, where people live to a 100 or more on a diet of lean meat, fresh vegetables and fruit (especially apricots). Examples like this, taken from the Himalayas, Caucasus and Andes, are interesting in themselves. Remember, however, that these long-lived people dwell at a high altitude and pursue a simple life of manual work. If we lived that sort of life, we — or anyway, our descendants — might live as long. It is a question, however, whether that is a helpful conclusion. We have our lives to live at a lower altitude and doing our own sort of work.

We may conclude from these examples that our diet is wrong, our soil impoverished and our cooking destructive. We might suspect that unstrained honey contains something of great value. But living the simple life in the high mountains would not maintain the sort of civilisation we have. Nor could the mountain valleys support a sudden increase of health-seeking immigrants. All we could achieve by going there would be to destroy the sort of life we had come there to study and pursue.

We should not forget about people who live the simple life in the high mountains, but we must agree, surely, that our concern must be with people like ourselves whose lives are still controlled by the civilisation of which we form a part. Let us assume that we still have to earn our living in London or Washington. Why should we want to live longer, not merely individually but as a group? To that question there is a simple answer but it applies to only a few people. Given the complexity of our civilisation, those who do the most specialised work take longer and longer to learn their trade and reach the point at which they can make their own contribution. There may be people who are, say, fifty before they have learnt all of their subject that is known. If they are obliged to retire at sixty-five, that gives them an effective top-level life of fifteen years. It must seem small as compared with the forty years or so spent in preparation. It must seem wasteful to discard someone at sixty-five to whose training so much time and effort have been devoted. This is more especially true of the research scientist or literary man. We might agree that it would be useful to prolong the life of men who have so much to contribute. Does the same argument apply to people who fill a humbler role? A bricklayer lays his bricks or a shop assistant sells his groceries from the age of fifteen or twenty to the age of sixty-five. Give him an extra thirty years, following the forty-five years of his working life and what is he to do with it? Lay more bricks or sell more groceries? Or should he do nothing for thirty years? We are driven to conclude that a longer life, if attainable, will be reserved for those who want it.

Let us suppose that the reader of this book is an executive who can look forward to retirement at sixty-five, or even earlier. What shall he do with the remaining years? Go for a cruise round the world? Very well, there is one year gone. What now? Play golf? Very well, he plays golf for four years. He then reaches the age at which, on average, we must expect to die. But what about his playing golf for thirty years? Does this really make any sense? For people who live on the managerial level the decision we may have to take is this: should we live until 90 or 100, being as difficult to replace as George Bernard Shaw, or should we group ourselves with the bricklayer whose bricklaying life is over? We shall have a choice to make and it is not as simple a decision as it might seem.

That each generation should live a little longer than the last would fit in, perhaps, with our ideas of progress. That there should be continued improvement is a doctrine we may have learnt in childhood. Such a concept is unknown, however, to archaeology or history. From all we know of the past we must conclude that civilisations rise and fall in a curve. Within each civilisation the different communities (cities, provinces, nations, empires) rise and fall in a curve of their own. Within the history of each community the lives of men follow the curve which is already known to all of us, at least as a general principle, but which we may not be able to apply to ourselves. To increase the life span of the useful and effective individual may also tend to increase the life span of the community. To increase the life span of the community should tend to increase the life span of the civilisation. And we might agree that this is desirable, postponing the decline and possibly adding to the height of its achievements. If we can assume that this is desirable, we have a basis of agreement on which to proceed. Some might think that it would be still more desirable if we were to avoid the decline indefinitely, going onward and upward forever as our school teachers may have assumed that we would. All one can say about that idea is that the past offers us no example of it. What it offers is the picture of successive curves, and one's assumption must be that what has happened before is happening now and will happen again. There may be no logic in supposing that winter must follow autumn and that spring must follow winter, but our experience leads us to expect the rhythm to continue. We have no reason to suppose that our own civilisation is different in this from any other. That it had its rise we know. That it will have its fall we may surely assume. On the other hand it seems possible that we might, by our efforts, postpone the decline which is to be foreseen. That effort might well be worth making for our children's sake. There would seem to be no special merit in waiting passively for the flood of barbarism which threatens to engulf us.

We should not wait passively but what should we do? It would be reasonable to ask what went wrong with previous civilisations. The last collapse we know about was that of Rome. About the history of its decline and fall we know a great deal. But why did it decline? Why did it fall? Of a tree we should say that it had reached the end of its expected life. It had ceased to grow. It had begun to decay. If the same could be said of mankind we should still want to know something about that decay. Had it some immediate and known cause? Could anything be done now?

The purpose of this book is to suggest that there is some useful action we could take. The authors do not mean to suggest that the secret to longevity has been wholly revealed to them. Much research is in progress and there must be many discoveries still to make. Of one thing we can be fairly sure and it is this: that the problem of greater longevity is not one to solve as individuals. There is little point in living after all our contemporaries have died. If we are to live longer we must share that privilege with some other people. We must realise, moreover, that a longer life means a complete reorganisation of society, with some implications which are fairly obvious and others which we probably cannot foresee. Before seeking to lengthen human life, we need to think carefully about what we are doing and with what possible results. In this book we do not pretend to give all the answers. We seek merely to contribute something to the general stock of ideas on an important subject. If we have added anything of value our effort will not have been in vain.

Chapter 1

Erosion

Each civilisation has its genesis, its immaturity, its peak of achievement, its middle and late period, its decline and its fall. Each community within a civilisation has a similar life cycle. Each individual within a community must follow the same path, and each tree has a similar life pattern from its first appearance to its final decay. This is the Law of Life and it has so far admitted of no exception. Youth among men has been the period of enthusiasm and energy, marred by inexperience and folly. Middle age has been the period of solid achievement, marred by excessive caution and doubt. Old age has brought wisdom but this has been marred by impotence and sloth. Only for a brief period can we combine energy with caution and both with wisdom. And what is true of men is no less true of each civilisation, of each community. Of early ages we may not know the exact sequence of events, but we can point to the fragments of architecture and art, distinguishing between the crude but vigorous, the strong yet graceful, the polished but uninspired, the careless and dull. Nor can we doubt that the sequence is inevitable, the consequence of our being what we are. Our only way to greater achievement has been to continue our efforts as best we might; the old to foresee, the mature to plan and the young to execute. But such a deployment of our talents, if sometimes successful among men, is not applicable to a community, still less to a civilisation.

The years of man are three score and ten, with little change since the Psalmist made that discovery. It is a question whether that life span was ever adequate, but changes in our way of life have made it progressively less convenient. Writing in 1920, George Bernard Shaw agreed with Weismann that death is not a basic condition of life but an expedient design to provide renewal without overcrowding. He postulated that decay and death are more or less voluntary and that man's life span has been a mistake from the outset.

> *Even our oldest men do not live long enough: they are, for all the purposes of high civilisation, mere children when they die: and our Prime Ministers, though rated as mature, divide their time between the golf course and the Treasury Bench in parliament.*
>
> *Conceivably, however, the same power that has taken us thus far can take us farther. If Man now fixes the term of his life at three score and ten years, he can fix it at three hundred or three thousand ... Surely our ruinous world wars should convince him of the necessity of at least outliv-*

*ing his taste for golf and cigars if the race is
to be saved.*

> George Bernard Shaw
> *Back to Methuselah*
> 1947, Galaxy ed., p. xvi

Shaw illustrated this theme by living until
the age of ninety-four, remaining active to the
end. He is probably the only author to have had
a new play performed after his 90th birthday.
He said once: "To live is normal; to die is abnor-
mal. I intend to go on living well over two hundred years." So he might have done but for an
accident in which he broke his thigh. Kept in
bed, he ceased to enjoy life and was dead in a
few days. But if he could say (in 1920) that men
do not live long enough, with what greater conviction can we echo his opinion in, say, 1980?
For while men may not have grown in wisdom
over that period, it is certain that they have
produced, among them, an ever-growing mass
of technical information. It takes longer and
longer to master all that is known in any particular field of knowledge. Men are apt to ex-
haust themselves in the process, having no
energy left to go on from there. Even those with
vitality unimpaired have all too short a remaining life in which to make their own contribution.
It is plain, therefore, that there is an ever-
lengthening distance from the pit shaft to the

coal face; and what is difficult for the budding lawyer or surgeon is doubly difficult for the novice politician whose field of knowledge should be so much wider. The late Poet Laureate, John Masefield, chose the title *So Long to Learn* for a volume of autobiography, sensing the fact that death would come before he had even completely mastered his trade. All who grow old must have the same awareness of the curtain falling before the play has ended and sometimes indeed before the first act has fairly begun. To live longer would be useless in itself, but to remain active over a lengthened life would be progress.

What is true of the individual may be as true of civilisation itself. Could we not achieve more over a longer span of years? What if youthful vigour could be maintained for centuries, overlapping the years of maturity? What if the peak of achievement could be sustained for a lifetime rather than for a mere decade? What if the golden autumn could be prolonged for centuries, with winter for as long postponed? These are not idle dreams if Shaw was right and if longevity is, at least partly, a matter of will. There is, however, at least one other factor to consider and that is the question of diet. Throughout the story of man there has been a tendency for cities to outgrow their immediate food supply, ruining their hinterland by soil erosion and seeking to avoid famine by trade or conquest. But food brought from a distance tends to lose its value in transit and people who live on it must tend to lose their vitality. This dietary deficiency seldom falls, however, on rich and poor alike. It is the lower classes whose energy first declines, the more prosperous folk being decadent perhaps in a different way.

Of many ancient civilisations we know too little to state with any certainty that their decline was due to a lack of mettle in their pastures. It is clear, nevertheless, that countries once fertile can no longer support the population they formerly had. Iran, which once had a population of forty million, has now little more, perhaps, than twenty-five. Palestine, which would seem to have had a population of about three million in the time of King David, had only 750,000 in 1910. In these and other countries, land formerly wooded, watered and productive has turned into desert.

As the centre of civilization moved westward the towns with growing population repeated the process of devouring the fertility of the country which had helped to bring about the downfall of the older civilization. Plato gives the following description of what took place in Greece: "At the period, however, of which we are dealing, when Attica was still intact, what are now her mountains were lofty soil-clad hills; her so-called shingle plains of the present day were full of rich soil; and her mountains were heavily afforested — a fact of which there are still visible traces. There are mountains in Attica which can now support nothing but bees, but which were clothed, not so long ago, with fine trees, producing timber suitable for roofing the largest buildings; the roofs hewn from the timber are still in existence. There were also many lofty cultivated trees, while the country produced boundless pastures for cattle. The annual supply of rainfall was not lost, as it is at present, through being allowed to flow over the denuded surface into the sea ... The shrines that survive to the present day on the sites of extinct water supplies are evidence ... "

Athens solved its food problems for a time by developing an export trade with a corresponding import of food. Sparta solved it by the conquest of adjoining lands. Greece, which once supported a prosperous nation, with a level of culture and creative intellectual life which has never been surpassed by any State, is now a poverty-stricken country with barren hills and poor soil, which gives an average yield of wheat of only twelve bushels — about a fourth of the yield of moderately good land.

John Boyd Orr
The White Man's Dilemma
London, 1953, p. 63, et seq.

EROSION

Much of the Greek population moved, in fact, to colonies elsewhere in Sicily, Italy and Asia Minor. Then the whole sequence began again in Rome, a city which grew powerful and soon outgrew the local supply of food. The Romans turned to North Africa, large areas of which were covered by forest. This land they conquered, founding cities there of which the fragments remain, dating in some instances from the time of Trajan. The land was deforested, the fields were overcropped, soil erosion followed, and the whole area is now a barren tract of shifting sand. The Roman economy could not survive but what was the result while the system appeared to work? We know all too little about it, but we must suspect that there were two forces at work, the first a loss of nutrition due to the impoverishment of the soil, the second a further loss due to the time each grain cargo spent in transit. The Roman proletariat was fed at the public expense, but what sort of a rabble did it finally become? Our problem here is to measure the possible malnutrition of people who may have been neither hungry nor actually ill. Some diseases leave a recognisable trace, but what proof can we find of a general lack of stamina and enterprise? Decadence is a fact apparent in politics and war, in literature and art, but can we say with confidence that malnutrition is the cause? That would be going too far, perhaps, but it would seem to be at least significantly coincident.

To take the story further, in broadest outline, the centre of power moved away from the impoverished Mediterranean. The western countries assumed the leadership in turn, basing their enterprise on a colder climate with a heavier rainfall and a mixed system of agriculture which conserved and indeed improved the soil. This would not have saved the land indefinitely from the pressure of population but the situation was saved, in the short term, by emigration and by the inflow of food from the Americas and Australasia. This saved the mixed farming and the landscape of Britain, preserving a country suitable for fox-hunting. The timber from North America saved the forests of Europe. But saving the European countryside meant ruining the plains of the New World.

North America was not so fortunate. The virgin land, instead of being cultivated on the European system was "mined". There seemed little need to conserve either forest or land where, in proportion to the population, there was such abundance of both. But by the beginning of the present century the Americans had reached the Pacific, and there was no more virgin land to be ravaged. In 1935 the alarm caused by the realization of the creation of the "dust

*bowl" led to the setting up of a Govern-
ment soil conservation service. The Report
of this service stated that half of the
original forest had been cut down or
burned, and the rate of destruction was still
going up, three trees being cut down for
every two planted. About a quarter of the
original arable and grazing land had been
rendered completely infertile or severely
damaged, and the loss of the top-soil from
cultivated land was going on at the rate of
3,000 million tons a year. Such was the
magnitude of the destruction ... in little
more than one hundred years. This destruction had proceeded at such an unprecedent-
ed rate because the timber, cotton and
wheat were consumed by the rapidly growing cities of Europe, in addition to what
was absorbed by the even more rapidly
growing cities of America.*

Orr, *op. cit.*

It is said that man has destroyed as many
productive acres as now exist, perhaps 8,000
million acres of the 12,000 million now
classified as desert. Yet other vast areas, still
under cultivation, have a yield declining in
quality and bulk. These are facts which may go
some way to explain the defeat of armies and
the collapse of empires. Of precise evidence we
have little until the time of World War I. This

involved the medical examination of two and a half million potential conscripts in the Britain of 1917-18, with a result which was described in these words:

> *Of every nine men of military age in Great Britain, on the average three were perfect, fit and healthy; two were on a definitely inferior plane of health and strength, whether from some disability or some failure of development; three were incapable of undergoing more than a very moderate degree of physical exertion and could almost (in view of their age) be described with justice as physical wrecks; and the remaining man was a chronic invalid with a precarious hold on life.*

John Burnett
Plenty and Want, p. 166

What is important to realise is that the generation of 1914-18 was probably better nourished than many previous generations had been. In the preceding years and still more in the aftermath of World War I, there was also a great deal of remedial work, beginning with the School Meals Act of 1906 and continuing with the supply of milk to schools from 1934, but the statistics for the period of World War II were still depressing:

... In the last year of the war 41 percent of the men medically examined were in C.3 condition although in the prime of life. This might have been put down to wartime rationing, nervous strain or other temporary causes, but these did not obtain in 1935 when no less than 62 percent of volunteers were found to be below the comparatively low standard of physique required by the Army (a percentage which rose to 68 percent in the industrial areas of the north). Were so many of the population living, if not in actual disease, at least "below par"; unable to lead full and useful lives and always a potential liability to the community?

Burnett, *op. cit.*, p. 241

They were and they probably are and we might go on to conclude that the same has been true of other populations in the past and that this has always been the background to decadence. Going further, we might guess that the greatest efforts, whether in war or trade, whether in engineering or art, have usually sprung from the soil which has not been impoverished, from a people with vitality unimpaired by malnutrition and from the sort of leadership which an energetic and virile people might choose to support.

Western civilisation has been in a state of decay since about 1900. This is a very broad generalisation and it cannot be equally true of every country. Britain's period of leadership ended rather abruptly in about 1905; the French effort ended sooner; the Americans retained their momentum for long enough to reach the moon. But the Western world, with Russia perhaps excepted, has lost the initiative, and the Oriental world has been renascent since the beginning of the century. The Japanese victory in the Russo-Japanese War, followed by the Chinese Revolution of 1911, marked the beginning of Oriental recovery. The French and the American defeats in Vietnam represent a further stage in the process. We can foresee a future in which we may lack the military power of the Chinese. Some realisation of this trend has induced us to accept some measure of European unity. This is plainly essential but it is as important, perhaps, to study the nature of our own decay. What is its immediate cause? Can we delay its progress or minimise its impact? The subject is a vast one and little research has been done.

The result is that this book must ask more questions than its authors can hope to answer. Even to ask the questions is, however, something. Seeing the contrast between energetic people and tired people, we cannot but ask why? On the one side, we have to consider the difference between one people and another. On the other hand, we have to consider the difference, within a people, between one group and another; as, for example, between the rich and the poor or between the north and the south. Some broad conclusions may be based on the known facts of soil erosion but detailed comparisons of diet are more difficult to interpret.

Take India as our first example. This is a country of which the central government, such as it was, collapsed in 1707. After a conflict between British and French, the subcontinent was brought under British rule and so remained until after World War II. That a mere handful of soldiers could maintain an alien government for about two centuries was partly due to Indian disunion but far more due to Indian decadence and soil erosion. Of the effects of soil erosion there is no doubt at all.

When in the fourth century B.C. Alexander the Great entered India by the Khyber Pass and marched his army to Karachi, the land was said to be well wooded. Soil erosion has taken its toll, and today archaeologists are finding in the desert of Sind relics of what must have been an advanced state of civilization. About two thousand years later the Emperor Jahanjir recorded in his memoirs that when he built the castle Namur for Queen Nurjehan, the forests were so thick that a bird could hardly spread its wings. Today there is nothing

*but denuded hill-country, with a few tufts
of grass and thorn-bushes, on which goats
eke out a miserable existence. That has
happened in about 300 years. The process is
still continuing. The Rajasthen Desert is
said to be creeping southward at the rate of
a mile a year, destroying fertile land faster
than land is being reclaimed elsewhere.*

Orr, *op. cit.*, p. 63

By lowering the death rate, the British
rulers of India made the situation infinitely
worse, finally creating the problem of Calcutta,
a nightmare situation to which there is no
humanitarian solution. But if British medicine
was disastrous in some of its effects, its practitioners were at least observant. They pointed
out, to begin with, that the Indian races varied
considerably in their standards of physique.

Writing in about 1919, McCay remarked
that anyone passing from the Punjab to the
Bengal coast would notice a gradual fall in the
stature, weight, stamina and efficiency of the
people. He concluded that the physique of the
northern races is strikingly superior to that of
the southern, eastern and western races. He attributed this superiority to their having a more
nutritious diet. A quarter of a century later Sir
Robert McCaruson came to the same conclusion. He pointed out that the races of northern

India live on whole wheat in the form of chapattis, milk and milk products, pulse, vegetables and fruit, to which some of them add meat. So far as physique is concerned they are, he maintained, among the finest races of mankind. In southern India the diet centres on rice (parboiled, milled and polished) and includes little in the way of vegetables or fruit and the physique of the people is correspondingly poor. He placed the diets of the Indian races in this order of nutritive value: Sikh, Pathan, Maharatta, Goorkha, Kanarese, Bengali and Madrassi. In this list the four "martial" races come first, the rice-eating southerners being relatively nowhere. He explained that rice is a poor cereal at best, that the process of polishing deprives it of most of its protein and mineral salts and that the Bengalis and Madrassis, being vegetarians, have little protein in any other form.

So far the argument would seem to be conclusive, but we must remember, first of all, that McCaruson's emphasis is on physique alone. There is no reason to believe that the southern Indians are lacking in brains, and we know in fact that they are not. Another awkward fact is that fine soldiers, and many recent general officers, have come from a small hill state in the south called Coorg. Still more to the point, any treatise on the dangers of polished rice must include some mention of the Japanese. It is true that rice in Japan has been increasingly "unpolished" since about 1912, but the fact remains that boiled rice has been the staple diet since the Nara or Buddhist period (710-784) and that the Japanese cannot be accused of idleness or inertia. The explanation would seem to be that few parts of Japan are far from the sea and that fish, including raw fish (sashimi), has always played a part in their diet. To this they have added vegetables, eggs and fowl, with bean-paste soup (misoshiru), boiled lentils with soya and, latterly, beef, veal, pork and mutton. There is supposed to be a difference in diet between the general regions east and west of the mountains, the contrast being between the Kuanto food characteristic of Edo (near Tokyo) and the Kwansai food which developed in Kyoto, once the seat of the Imperial Court. Be that as it may, the general picture is one of the rice diet, saved by the addition of vegetables and fish. But the Japanese had no knowledge of dietetics and fed their army at Port Arthur on a daily ration of 5 ounces of meat and 30 ounces of rice. The result was they had 200,000 cases of beri-beri. Their navy had formerly suffered in the same way and some warships had actually put back to port in 1882 with, in one instance, 195 men sick out of a crew of 330. The result was that Takaki, Medical Inspector-General of the Japanese Navy in 1880-90, insisted upon introducing a new daily ration which included meat, fish, barley, vegetables and milk. Beri-

beri disappeared at once, cured, as we now realise, by a certain element in the barley.

It is probable that there was always a difference between the diet, in Japan, of the noble and warrior classes and the diet of the people at large. This was always so in Britain but there, too, there was little talk about dietetics. It was merely a case of more prosperous people having what they liked and could afford, with more variety and more distinctive taste. There was, however, a general belief in the virtues of meat as an essential in the fighting man's diet. As Shakespeare makes his Frenchman in *King Henry V,* (Act III, Scene 7) say of the English: ". . . give them great meals of beef, and iron and steel, they will eat like wolves and fight like devils." Given enough and given variety, the right elements might well have been accidently included. There has never been such likelihood where the poor are concerned, and the British lower classes have tended, in recent history, to live on white bread, meat, potatoes and an all too generous quantity of refined sugar, much of it drunk in tea. On this sort of diet children are apt to suffer from poor appetites, poor growth, nervousness and constipation. As for adults, it was found at the Peckham Health Centre that 90 percent of the artisan class over 25 had some physical defect. Among the insured population in 1933, a total of 27,000,000 weeks of work was lost through illness. Nor has there been a dramatic improvement since more has come to be known about food values. Tooth decay, due to excess of starch and sugar, is still on the increase. There was much of it in Roman times. It fell to a lower level in Saxon England but has risen steeply since about 750 and more steeply still after 1900. There is much drivel currently about toothpaste and toothbrushes, but the fact is that dental caries can be traced to malnutrition. It is one aspect, in fact, of general health, which is itself mainly determined by diet.

Broad conclusions reached from a study of diet in Europe and Asia are reinforced by a study of diet in Africa. Dr. Le Compte, co-author of this book, was in the Belgian Congo from 1954 to 1957. He was at first assigned to the Leper Colony at Loango-Luvungu, his task being to look after three hundred lepers. He did better than that by curing them and was presently transferred, as medical director, to the general hospital at Kuimba, which served a population of 50,000 natives and looked after five hundred hospitalised patients at any one time and another two hundred out-patients daily. The hospital also cared for sick Europeans but these were relatively few in number. This may seem strange in that the whole of West Africa was once looked upon as the white man's grave. If the black slaves often died on the voyage to America, a high proportion of the white seamen died before the middle passage had so much as begun. Even today there are health risks in visiting the Congo and these risks multiply, no doubt, with the length of the stay. What Dr. Le Compte observed, however, was that the health hazard for the European was as nothing compared with the hazard confronting the black. It might be supposed that the native population would be acclimatised and accustomed to the humidity and heat. The Congo was their home, after all, and they had no other. It was they, nevertheless, who crowded the hospitals and it was their death rate which stood the higher. More than that, a proportion of those supposedly in good health were prematurely aged, inactive and weak.

West Africa is not a formerly fertile region which has been ruined by soil erosion. It is an equatorial jungle on the fringes of which there are plantations of oil palms, coffee, rubber and other crops for export. What it has never produced in any quantity is food. There is business enough, however, and more especially in copper mining, to bring prosperity to certain groups among the native population. There are everywhere, moreover, some tradesmen and others who can be classed, by native standards, as rich. Dr. Le Compte observed that these were almost as healthy as the Europeans. While exposed to all the same risks as anyone else, they were in better health, less subject to tropical disease, and lived to a greater age. Dr. Le Compte's conclusion was that their better health had nothing to do with hygiene, housing or clothes. The point was that they were better fed, most of their money going in fact on a more expensive and more varied diet. Reports published by the World Health Organisation pointed also to the conclusion that the natives as a whole were chronically underfed. But if the blacks in the Congo grow old more rapidly through under-nourishment, it seemed probable that this might be a factor in the process by which other people grow old. As against that, the process elsewhere could not be a matter of people going hungry, for hunger in many countries was clearly not the problem, and relatively short-lived people could be very prosperous indeed. The shortage must not be one, then, merely of food, but of some elements of nourishment which can be absent from an apparently satisfying diet. Dr. Le Compte's discovery was that aging proceeds more rapidly where the deficiencies of diet are greater and more numerous.

The contrast between the poor and the prosperous goes back, in fact, to the beginnings of recorded time. At the siege of Troy, according to Homer — who has so far proved right in such of his statements as are capable of proof — the actual fighting was mostly done by a limited number of known heroes. To judge from the *Iliad* (Penguin classics, 1949), the ordinary soldiers seldom closed with their opponents. Each leader in his chariot was backed up by a small formation of infantry. When his spears had been expended or his shield lost, the leader retired behind his men to recuperate or rearm. There were certain exceptions to this pattern because the Darnanians were said to "enjoy close fighting" (p. 283) and there was that moment when the Greeks had their backs to the sea, their ships in danger, and "the Achaeans and Trojans fought each other hand to hand." For once, in a way, it was no longer "a matter of holding off and standing up to a volley of arrows or of javelins" (p. 290). There was another occasion, incidentally, when Odysseus was surrounded by Trojan infantry, but they never dared close with him. They seem to have scattered in all directions as soon as Aias came to the rescue and Menelaus led Odysseus back to a waiting chariot. Agamemnon on an earlier occasion tried to shame the Argives into battle, exclaiming that "the whole crowd of us are no match for Hector alone" (p. 151). When Hector was finally killed, Achilles says of him that "he did more damage than all the rest together" (p. 407). The picture we have is of a conflict normally sustained by the biggest and strongest men, the acknowledged leaders, and the ordinary foot soldiers playing, at best, a strong supporting role.

It would seem fair to conclude that the leaders were better fed than the rest. During the actual campaign the Argives might gorge themselves "on the beef of straight-horned cattle" and drink from "bowls brimful of wine." But was this their ordinary fare? Homer tells us of feasts on special occasions with emphasis on beef, pork, bread and wine. But the poor man's meal may well have been different. In the later and classical period of Greek history the Greeks would seem to have lived on barley cakes made into porridge, with figs, olives and cheese made from the milk of ewes and goats. People could live healthily, no doubt, on that, but the men of wealth fared better and this must have been true in Homeric times. The heroes were also better armoured and armed and some of them, like Odysseus, were of exceptional intelligence; but Homer's insistence is on sheer brute strength. When without any other missile, the hero would always throw a stone such as no ordinary man could even lift. Thus when Hector smashed the gates of the Greek camp it was with a rock which "would have taxed the strength of the two best men in any city of these latter days to lever it up from the ground onto a cart." The stories have lost nothing in the telling but the impression remains, and is probably correct, that the leaders in war were the biggest, not necessarily the brainiest, of the tribe. Can we doubt that they also had a better and more varied diet?

From what information we have, based on different continents and different periods, we can perhaps identify decadence as a general state of indifferent health and reduced energy. Its basic cause may be malnutrition, which can result from one or more of three general conditions: pressure of population on a soil that has always been poor, soil erosion spoiling a soil that was formerly rich, or a faulty diet due merely to ignorance or superstition. West Africa is an example of the first condition, Greece and Rome were examples of the second and India affords examples of the third. But the general situation in any instance can be complicated by differences in diet between rulers and subjects, between rich and poor. Periods of decadence may be as inevitable as autumn and winter and it might be argued that peoples, like fields, must be allowed to lie fallow. As against that, the argument surely holds good that a longer life is becoming desirable. Were that accepted we must surely devote some effort to the study of decadence. If it has deeply rooted biological causes it may well be that we can do nothing about it. But what if its causes are at least partly dietetic? What if feebleness and inertia are the result of malnutrition? Here at least is an ailment for which there should be a remedy. The cure may not be as straightforward as one might expect, and there are grounds for thinking that it is not, but we should know in what area to begin the search. The subject is vast and we shall ask more questions than we answer, but we can urge the need for research and suggest that some effort should be devoted to it before the situation deteriorates much further. The present age is one which presents us with problems which we regard as complex, obscure and new. There is no problem, however, which could not be solved by people with sufficient energy and courage, especially if these qualities were accompanied by some historical knowledge and an increased longevity. Solutions would be reached even sooner, however, by people who can recognise a political problem when they see it; a recognition which would spare us a lot of twaddle about economics. The central institution of our present society is the motor car. When it refuses to start we are apt to swap theories about possible malfunctions and defects, shaking our heads over the ignition coil or the battery. It can sometimes happen, however, that the simplest explanation turns out to be the right one. It may be that our petrol tank is empty. All that ails us, perhaps, is that we have run out of gas.

CHAPTER 2

Diet

The Dark Ages were dark only in the sense that we know all too little about them. The classical world collapsed in Western Europe and barbarian tribes broke through the frontier. The numbers of these invaders were greatly exaggerated by the general officers that had failed to keep them out, giving later historians the problem of explaining where they had come from. They were, in fact, relatively few and they had no doubt previously infiltrated the frontier provinces they were later to attack.

The pattern of conquest, the occupation of arable lands by nomad tribesmen, is a familiar one throughout history. The success of the herdsmen has been attributed to their eating of meat and their drinking of mare's milk; as also their consumption of curd or yogurt, butter and cheese. At a later period the Arabs broke into Europe from a different direction, illustrating afresh the energy of the nomad and bringing with them a taste for mutton fat, yogurt and dates. When Western crusaders counter-attacked the Arabs with initial enthusiasm but with dwindling success, they often ended in hospital at Salerno.

It was there, in the late eleventh century, that there developed the Salerno regimen of health based on a mixture of Arabic ideas with other doctrines dating back to the times of Hippocrates and Galen. Then, as at other and more recent periods, the chief obstacle to scientific progress was not ignorance but the belief among educated people that they knew it all. In this way the Salerno regimen, which involved the rejection of fruit as liable to cause dysentery, was orthodox for centuries and must have done considerable harm.

Amidst all this nonsense was heard, at least faintly, the voice of Ibn Khaldun of Tunis (1332-1406) who pointed out the sequence by which dynasties rise and fall. Each begins with a movement from the desert, headed by people who are crude, poor, rancorous and enterprising. Once the new dynasty is established, no longer in the desert, the tribes become urbane, civilised, charitable and effete, ripe for destruction in their turn. Ibn Khaldun also noted that whole regions had been ruined by the Arabs, their population dispersed and even the soil itself apparently transformed. He attributed human energy to the avoidance of a rich diet. The Spaniards he cites as an example of a people "whose country produces no butter and who live mainly on millet and in whom we can observe a sharpness of mind and a readiness for learning and a bodily grace which are unique."

Ibn Khaldun may not have found the exact formula for success through a balanced diet but he had at least come to believe that the secret must exist.

A later theory about diet came from the pen of Luigi Cornaro, a contemporary of Titian, whose *Discorsi della Vita Sobria* was published at Padua in 1358:

> *Cornaro, a Venetian nobleman, was born in 1464 and lived about one hundred and two years, dying in 1566.*
>
> *In the first forty or so years of his life, Cornaro lived much as did his companions of the nobility, with the consequence that, at that age, he broke down completely and almost died — being saved only through an adoption of this habit he outlines and defends in his book THE TEMPERATE LIFE . . . Cornaro reduced his allowance of food to 12 oz. with 14 oz. light Italian wine — and on this diet he subsisted for practically the remainder of his wonderfully active and brilliant life . . .*

> Hereward Carrington
> *Vitality, Fasting and Nutrition,* p. 113

Cornaro ate all kinds of food but in small quantity, having four light meals a day and drinking more moderately as he grew older. It should perhaps be emphasised that he was prescribing for the elderly. As against that, he had perceived the connection between diet and health and had ideas which were quite sensible. He knew little or nothing about food values, however, and made no contribution to the solutions of the chief dietetic problem of his age, the problem of scurvy.

In the Middle Ages merchant ships were employed on relatively short voyages, within the Mediterranean, the Baltic or on the Atlantic route which connected the two inland seas. They were seldom remote from land and seldom at sea for more than two or three weeks at a time. Food preservation had not been a big problem and the health of seamen had not been, in itself, a subject for study. With the discovery of America and the opening of the sea route to India, there was an entirely new situation. Voyages could be prolonged up to a period of six months with no landfall for many weeks at a time. How were ships to be provisioned for that sort of voyage? It did not take long to decide that diet on the long voyage should centre upon salt beef and biscuit, neither a new invention. These were foods which would keep for a sufficient time, but it soon transpired that men placed on such a diet would go sick with scurvy, a disease not unknown ashore. The cure for scurvy was to enter harbour and send the sick men ashore. Given fresh food they would soon recover.

In the tropics, however, the harbour was dangerous in another way, the seamen being now afflicted very likely with yellow fever or malaria. The cure for malaria was to put to sea once more, with renewed danger of scurvy. The cause of the fever was believed to be "bad air" (hence malaria) and there was little anyone could do about it. The cause of scurvy was seen to be a deficiency of diet. Efforts were begun to discover a food or drink which would prevent scurvy.

A first remedy lay in the brewing of spruce beer, a technique learnt by Cartier from the Indians along the St. Lawrence. This was not without some value but a far better remedy resulted from Lancaster's voyage in 1601. This was the drinking of lemon juice, already recommended by Sir Richard Hawkins in 1593. The astonishing sequel is that the value of lemon juice was then forgotten, all sorts of remedies being tried over the next two hundred years.

After the disastrous casualties of Anson's voyage in 1740-44 (1,051 men dead out of 1,955 embarked), Dr. Richard Mead published his *Discourse on the Scurvy* in 1749, advising the issue of wine-vinegar as a substitute for sub-acid fruits. Soon afterwards Dr. James Lind wrote his more scientific *Treatise of the Scurvy* (1753), stating that spruce beer, pickled cabbage and sauerkraut might be useful but that oranges and lemons were best of all. Lind was not, unfortunately, the only one to suggest a remedy for scurvy and the Admiralty recommended the use of malt made into wort. The result was that ships at sea during the early years of the War of American Independence were sometimes seriously undermanned, the result of heavy mortality and sickness.

But the turning point, so far as scurvy was concerned, came in 1780 when Admiral Rodney took over the command of the American and West Indies Station. With Rodney was Gilbert Blane, initially as his personal physician but soon afterwards as Physician of the Fleet. Dr. Blane found that the Fleet had a mortality rate of 1 in 7. He issued new instructions about hygiene and emphasised the value of lemons. The practice had been to heat lemon juice before bottling it, thus destroying its value. He advised against this and generally formed an opinion about the maintenance of health at sea. He returned to England with Rodney, coming back with the admiral in 1781. That year great efforts had been made to man, equip and supply the fleet, and the health statistics were improving:

In the flagship not a man died in four months and only 13 were sent to hospital. "This ship," wrote Blane proudly, after the efforts he had made at home to have her perfectly fitted out, "left England with

*everything that could be supposed to con-
duce to the health of the men and may be
considered as an experiment to prove what
degree of health may be attained by proper
management and attention."*

Christopher Lloyd and J. L. S. Coulter
Medicine and the Navy, Vol. III, p. 133

This improved state of health at sea was an important factor in Rodney's victory at the Battle
of the Saints. It also resulted in Dr. Blane's
becoming, as Sir Gilbert, a Commissioner for
Sick and Hurt, which office he held soon after
the next war began in 1793. Blane's efforts on
shore were complemented by those of Dr.
Thomas Trotter at sea. Trotter had been physician at Haslar Hospital and was Physician to
the Channel Fleet under Lord Howe. He was
also the author of *Observations on Scurvy*
(1786), which book shows that he was essentially a disciple of Lind. By 1795 Blane had per-
suaded the Admiralty to sanction an issue of
lemon juice which would provide 3/4 oz. lemon
and 2 oz. of lemon sugar to be mixed with 1 pint
of water and 1/2 pint of rum. By 1804, on the
eve of Trafalgar, 50,000 gallons of lemon juice
were being consumed each year. At the same
time, the other preventions and remedies went
out of fashion.

Speaking of the decade before 1795, Trotter says that "for the prevention of scurvy the British Navy is at present supplied with Sauerkraut, Elixir of Vitriol, Malt and Essence of Wort," and he proceeds to demolish the value of each in turn. The introduction of the first was due to Lind, inspired by the practice of the Dutch Navy; but, says Trotter, fresh salad is better and sauerkraut is not worth the expense which it has cost the government: "its virtues as an antiscorbutic are very trifling." Vitriol was due to Dr. Huxham of Plymouth: as far as scurvy is concerned, it is "a mere placebo." Malt, and the wort made from it, was due to MacBride and Pringle, and was so well reported on that it became a regular issue, but for his part, says Trotter, "I have not seen it attended with any good effects," though like Lind he admits its nourishing value... It seems, concludes Trotter, that "fresh, essential vegetables of all kinds will cure it, but those fruits abounding with an acid, such as the citric class, are more effective than others.

Lloyd & Coulter, *op. cit.,* Vol. III, p. 323

Trotter was essentially right and scurvy had been conquered, at least for the time being. Only two cases were treated at Haslar during the last four years of the war, all the rest being cured on board ship. The lemons in general use came from Sicily and from countries in the Mediterranean. Ships in the West Indies were often supplied, however, with limes, which were locally obtainable. In order to reduce the expense, the cheaper limes became a general issue in 1860 having already been adopted by the East India Company and eventually made a compulsory issue in all merchantmen. The fact that lime juice is more or less valueless as an antiscorbutic was not immediately apparent because the general diet had greatly improved and because steamship voyages did not take so long as voyages under sail. Tinned and canned food was imported as an alternative to salt beef and pork. Then cases of scurvy were reported by Sir George Nares, commanding the *Alert* and *Discovery* on an arctic voyage in 1875-76. There were, during the one winter, sixty cases and three deaths out of 122 men, and the lime juice issued proved ineffective. Even after this experience a Committee of Inquiry stated its continued belief in lime juice. The exact causes of scurvy were not established, in fact, until after World War I, and there were outbreaks of the disease on board American ships during World War II.

There were many theories about diet in nineteenth and early twentieth-century Europe but few with any scientific basis. A typical theorist was Alexander Haig who published his book on *Diet and Food* in 1898 and published the second edition in 1906 seeing in dietetics a new hope for mankind:

> ... *I believe I speak no more than the truth when I say that once a clear knowledge of the facts is possessed and a workmanlike and useful grasp of the subject attained, it will be found that in diet lies the key to nine-tenths of the social and political problems which vex our nation and time.*"
>
> p. viii

Having made this bold claim he goes on to explain that:

> ... *the first requisite for strength and power of endurance is a satisfactory and sufficient supply of albumens, that the body depends for these chiefly on the foods taken but there is also a small store of these substances in certain tissues which becomes available if prolonged exertion is called for in the absence of food and beyond this point in continued starvation, certain definite quantities of the tissues themselves are daily absorbed to produce the necessary force and urea.*
>
> p. 29

Haig's solution to the problem of diet was to exclude the eating of meat. There was at this period some talk about vegetarianism and even some actual experiment, and Haig was able to quote the following news item from the Berlin correspondent of the *Daily News,* printed June 29, 1898:

> *It stated that fourteen meat-eaters and eight vegetarians started for a 70 mile walking match. All the vegetarians reached the goal "in splendid condition," the first conquering the distance in fourteen and a quarter hours. An hour after the last vegetarian came the first meat-eater and he was "completely exhausted." He was also the last meat-eater, for all the rest had dropped off after 35 miles . . .*
>
> *An almost exactly similar illustration of the effects of diminished function is furnished by the Dresden to Berlin walk of 1902. For this eighteen vegetarians and fourteen meat-eaters started, and ten vegetarians, but only three meat-eaters came in. The winner (Karl Mann) was finished seven hours before the meat-eaters.*
>
> *The last meat-eater was only just in within the time limit and was beaten by more than four hours by a man of 59, who had been a vegetarian for thirty-eight years.*

Haig, *op. cit.,* p. 106

These results may or may not be considered sufficient proof that vegetarianism is best, but on this subject Alexander Haig had no doubt at all:

Again, if the muscles produce force more smoothly and continuously, and with less friction, on a supply of albumens free from the poisonous products of dead animal tissues and if muscular life becomes more pleasant from this cause, how much more important this physiological solvency, when we realise that it applies to the great nerve centres, the organ of the mind and find that here also the result is better work more easily performed, and not only this, but a more kindly, true and noble relation to all the conditions and phenomena of life.

This is seen even in the ordinary mental attitude of meat-eaters.

Meat-eating (or for that matter uric acid taking in any form) induces laziness, since it brings about a sluggish, defective circulation in brain, muscle, bone and throughout the body: hence people are what is called "bone lazy," but are really brain, bone, muscle and generally lazy, because circulation is everywhere defective. Others say that they are "born tired," which means that they were born full of uric acid by a parent who was full of it.

This means selfishness, effeminacy, degeneration, decay and extinction, if continued. It produces the love of riches that a luxurious idleness may be attained. Whether this, with its consequent satiety and distaste for life, is the ideal for the unit of a healthy nation, let the nation judge.

Anaemia, lethargy, selfishness, degeneration of mind and body (which are all forms of disease) abound, few or none know what healthy life means, and the great majority live but half their span. The ways are full of the lethargic who do not want to walk, the arthritic with crippled joints who cannot walk and the obese who can only crawl.

To those who are free from disease, life presents a very different aspect, all is energy, labour is a glory, the power to do is a pleasure; theirs is the healthy instinct for longevity and indolence offers no attractions.

The one attitude of mind is sanity and health; the other disease, degeneration, insanity and death . . .

Ibid., p. 128

By way of commenting on this stirring passage one should remark, first of all, that albumen is a nutritious substance surrounding a developing embryo such as the white of an egg or the material stored in a plant seed. In further comment one might concede that Haig was writing at the exact period when the British seem to have exhausted their energy.

And, whatever the arguments there may be for and against vegetarianism, he would seem to have hit on a truth in discovering that health and longevity are derived from an attitude of mind. Whether or not all evil can be traced to uric acid we may admit that health begins with the will to live.

The scientific study of diet began in the aftermath of World War I. Rationing systems during the war drew attention to dietetic needs and the end of the conflict revealed the results of famine. British strategy involved the effective blockade of Central Europe, where the populations were finally living on black bread and potatoes. Medical investigation discovered that rickets were common, that the death rate from tuberculosis had increased by 70 percent, that 60 percent of the children showed signs of arrested growth and 40 percent had tuberculous glands. As the cease-fire was brought about by an armistice (or truce) rather than by the preliminaries of a peace treaty, the blockade actually continued after the fighting had stopped. As for Russia, defeated and then upset by revolution, the conditions there were no better than in Germany. As late, indeed, as 1923 some thirteen million cases of malaria were reported from southern Russia as compared with three and a half million before the war. This was an ideal period for the study of famine. Fortunately for the medical men concerned, a great deal of work had been done before the war. Thanks to Justus von Liebig it had been known since 1846 that food is composed of carbohydrates, fats and "albuminoids" or protein. It then appeared that certain minerals are included. It was apparent however, that there must be other elements, not yet identified. It was the Dutch physician, Christian Eijkman, who solved this problem in 1901 while attempting to find the cause of beri-beri. Hens developed this disease when fed on polished rice but recovered when given the 'bran' which had been removed in the polishing. There was therefore an important food element in the bran — the rice germ itself.

... and even then scientists failed to realise that what had been discovered was, in effect, a whole new class of food components, some of which were essential in themselves, and others which had to be present before the human body could, for example, convert carbohydrates into energy, or utilize particular minerals. In 1905 Professor Pekelharing at the University of Utrecht came to the conclusion that some such "unrecognized substance" did exist, and in 1909, a German biochemist, Dr. Stepp — without fully realizing it at the time — identified those vitamins which are fat-soluble. Just before the First World War vitamins A and B were effectively isolated.

Reay Tannahill
Food in History
New York, 1973, pp. 375-376

The word "vitamin" was coined in 1911 by a Polish scientist, Dr. Casimi Funk, while working at the Lister Institute in London. He chose the word "vita" because the substance discovered in rice polishings — which prevented beri-beri — was evidently essential to life. His work was largely duplicated in Malaya by the work of Fraser and Stanton. As if to illustrate this discovery came General Townshend's campaign in 1915-16. His attack on Ctesiphon failed and he was surrounded by the Turks at Kut-el-Amara. White troops were reduced to a diet of horseflesh, bread and oatmeal, and Indian troops to barley flour, barley ghee (native butter) and dates. The British suffered from beri-beri, lacking vitamin B; the Indians suffered from scurvy from lack of vitamin C. The British were saved from scurvy by horseflesh, the Indians from beri-beri by barley. The disaster was complete, however, and Townshend was forced to surrender, the victim of vitamin deficiency. Vitamin C was not, in fact, isolated and identified until 1932.

The vitamins more familiar to the dietician are lettered from A to E but with subdivisions. It is now recognised that the elements in food, like carbohydrates, which provide calories or warmth, are useless without vitamins. It is also known that vitamins overlap in function so that a deficient diet cannot result from the absence of a single vitamin. There is a final complication due to the fact that vitamins, consumed by people whose diet has been deficient, are not necessarily absorbed. It is also necessary to remember that vitamins originally present in food can be destroyed by cooking. While recognizing these and other limiting factors, we could nevertheless present a very simplified list of vitamins which is not too misleading and which is the key to much else in this book. If this is carefully studied and memorised there should be no difficulty in grasping the basic theory of dietetics, the importance of which — whether to the individual, the community or the civilization — must now be obvious.

TABLE

Vitamin	Function to Provide	Ailments Due To A Deficiency Of	Foods Which Contain It
A	Reproduction Growth	Night-blindness	Vegetables Fish Livers Egg Yolk Milk Butter Cheese

continued

Vitamin	Function to Provide	Ailments Due To A Deficiency Of	Foods Which Contain It
B_1	Energy	Beri-Beri Anaemia Indigestion	Whole Wheat Soya Bran Kidney Brewer's Yeast
B_2	Energy	Poor Vision Premature Aging	Whole Wheat Milk Buttermilk Liver Brewer's Yeast
Niacin	Courage	Pellagra Depression	Barley Beans Chicken Peanut Flour Brewer's Yeast Steak Hamburger
C	Vitality	Scurvy Tooth Decay (Pyorrhea) Tuberculosis Dysentery Hay Fever	Puerto Rican Cherry Rose Hips Other fruit, Oranges, Lemons Bean Sprouts Green Peppers
D	Energy	Tooth decay	Cod-liver Fish liver
E	Reproduction	Aging Sterility Rheumatism Loss of Sex Characteristics	Wheat Germ Cod-Liver Oil Shark-Liver Oil Milk (esp. Goat) Eggs Olives Palm Soyabeans Vegetables (peas etc.)

To this table two notes must be added. First, that vitamin C needs to be constantly replaced, being lost in the urine. Second, that while all the vitamins derive from food, vitamin D also derives from sunshine.

Armed with some such table as this, historians should look again at the rise and fall of civilisations and nations. Was there a dietetic side to even the best-known events in history? The task of establishing the facts could be immensely difficult but the result would surely justify the effort and would have a direct bearing on the future. At the moment we can do little more than ask questions. We learn that the Roman army suffered from scurvy. Was this a significant factor in any particular campaign? We learn that maize provided the staple diet in Aztec Mexico. Was pellagra a cause of the Spanish success? And what part had beri-beri to play in the history of what we now call Indonesia? A reduction in rations is said to have led to the Italian defeat at Caporetto. Sheer hunger is thought to have weakened the German armies in 1918. Historians who have been eloquent about religion and politics, about feudalism and the constitution, have been mostly silent about what people had for breakfast. It might appear, however, that diet is important and that deficiencies in diet may be more important still. We should also remember that there can be inefficiency without actual illness, that there can be a pre-scorbutic condition, that people not on the sick list can often be far from well. The world's medical history should be better known, and known especially to those who are medically qualified. It would teach them humility and help them realise how wrong their predecessors have been and how easy it is to be wrong again.

It would not be true to say that progress in dietetic science has made no impact on the world of today. For one thing, the experience of World War I was applied to the conduct of World War II.

. . . By 1939 health departments were providing milk, cod-liver oil, iron and vitamin products at low costs or free for clear cases of malnutrition in mothers and infants. The "Milk in Schools" scheme which had started in 1934 was supplying a third of a pint of milk daily to 50 percent of elementary school children, again at low cost or none at all, and had increased their consumption from none to twenty-two million gallons a year. Necessitous children and those clearly in need of extra nourishment were provided with midday meals at school, 5 percent of elementary school children benefiting from them. By 1939 there were three thousand Infant Welfare Centres under the supervision of the Ministry of Health. The results of these

policies were already impressive. Twelve-year-old boys attending elementary schools in London were three inches taller and eleven pounds heavier than their fathers had been twenty years earlier: equally important, an experiment sponsored by the Milk Nutrition Committee in 1938-39 demonstrated that school children receiving supplementary milk not only showed a general improvement in health but derived greater benefit from their lessons.

John Burnett
Plenty and Want: A Social History of Diet in England from 1815 to the Present Day
London, 1966, p. 256

So much was done before World War II and in unconscious preparation for it. After war began the same dietetic knowledge was applied to the rationing of both troops and civilians. By the end of 1943 there were 10,577 workers' canteens, providing a balanced diet for munition and other workers. There were over 2,000 British restaurants serving 615,000 midday meals for all who wanted them. There were improvements during the war in general health of children, and there was a significant reduction in infant mortality. By the end of the war the British were better fed, on an average, than they had ever been. That is not to say that their diet was or is perfect. A lower class diet of white bread, meat, potatoes, margarine, and refined sugar is deficient in vitamins and too little is spent on vegetables, butter and fruit. But things are better than they were in the world's industrialised countries, whatever doubts we may have about the future. There is, of course, a very different situation in poorer countries with an eroded soil and a rising level of population.

We must also note that solving the problem of diet, in so far as it has been solved, has created some problems hitherto unknown. Young people from a working class background, better fed than their ancestors, and too little exercised and occupied, may turn to hooliganism and crime. Older men who have never known hunger indulge more readily in industrial dispute. Boys reach sexual maturity at an earlier age, leaving us without trebles for the choir. A generation that is by previous standards sexually precocious seems to be, by the same standards, intellectually retarded. Improvements in diet are to be welcomed, but they are not everything and the outcome can be unexpected and even in some ways undesirable.

To summarize the conclusions we have reached, we must surely agree that diet has played an important role in past history, in the shaping of national character, in determining the results of human conflict. Diet has clearly affected energy and enterprise, procreation and courage. Those properly fed may well have better vision, stronger teeth, smoother digestion and greater longevity. They may well avoid many diseases. There is, on the other hand, no reason to suppose that they are more intelligent, more imaginative, more idealistic and more humane. Intellectual gifts appear to be almost entirely hereditary, and there is no evidence that inherited characteristics can be replaced or improved by changes in diet. Having admitted so much, however, we may still insist that vitality is important and that perseverance is vital to achievement. What we cannot maintain is that human beings have much natural instinct for feeding wisely. Those afflicted with scurvy do not instinctively clamour for lemon squash or salads. Those crippled by rheumatism have no natural addiction for cod-liver oil. People would seem rather to have eaten what is available, what they can afford, what they are used to and what they like, often in defiance of medical advice, often against all considerations of common sense, and often with the most unfortunate results.

During the first half of the twentieth century conditions changed. The age of science had dawned. It had been discovered that food, to be of value, must contain vitamins. It had been established that foods popular at table are often dietetically worthless or are even (like sugar) actually harmful. It became possible to measure food values and ensure a balanced diet for people living in barracks, hospitals, colleges and ships. It was not as possible, however, to ensure a nutritious diet in the home, for people in general were not to be advised. Proof of this is to be found in the relative failure of our efforts to discourage the smoking of cigarettes. Smoking has continued much as before even after everyone has been told of the health hazards involved. But people who can ignore warnings about lung cancer are most unlikely to accept guidance over their eating habits in which the dangers are less immediate and the dividends more remote.

At the same time there has been another and more significant change in the ordinary person's way of life. There was a time when people trudged to work, when children walked or cycled to school, when mothers tottered home with the shopping basket. But all this physical effort has been more or less abolished, the worker travelling by car, the children being driven by motor coach, the housewife going by bus. In the later twentieth century exercise is no longer the inevitable consequence of living in this place and working in that. Now the sidewalk is empty and the roads are full. In a motorised world exercise has become voluntary, a matter of taking part in or, anyway, watching some game that has been planned for a certain time and place. Where no such game has been organised and announced there is no need for physical exercise. Some people tend, therefore, to live without exertion but eat very much what an old-time farm labourer would have eaten had he been able to afford it. So this is an age of indigestion and worry, with "health shops," and constipation, with neuroses and aspirin. Despite some improvements in diet, we realise that this is an age of decadence, that there is to be no golden future and that the great days are definitely in the past.

CHAPTER 3

Decadence

Discussing the fall of the Roman Empire, Sir Kenneth Clark points out that civilisation, however, complex and solid it seems, is actually quite fragile:

> ... *It can be destroyed. What are its enemies? Well, first of all, fear — fear of war, fear of plague and famine, that make it simply not worthwhile constructing things, or planting trees ... and fear of the supernatural, which means that you daren't question anything. The late antique world was full of meaningless rituals, mystery religions, that destroyed self-confidence, and then exhaustion, the feeling of hopelessness which can overtake people even with a high degree of material prosperity.*
>
> *So if one asks why the civilisation of Greece and Rome collapsed, the real answer is that it was exhausted.*
>
> *Civilisation: A Personal View*
> London, 1969, pp. 3-4

That is, in effect, a good answer as far as it goes, but it gives rise to the further questions: Exhausted in what way? Exhausted by what ef-

fort? And why was it exhausted at that particular time? That their soil had been eroded
and that their food was deficient in vitamins is
at least possible and may well be the fact. That
they had suffered heavy casualties in war is
beyond question. That they had over-extended
their conquests is probably true. But is that the
whole truth? We know all too little about it.
Where we are on firmer ground is in defining
the symptoms, as opposed to the causes, of
decadence, for about these the facts are known.
Sir Kenneth Clark identifies decadence with
fear, with loss of confidence, with doubts about
the future. It is this distrust of the future which
limits the amount of thought and effort put into
any work of architecture or art. To spend two
hundred years in building a cathedral implies a
belief that it will be in use for a thousand years.
To spend ten years in painting a picture is
reasonable on the assumption that it will survive for at least a century. But what when the
future is more in doubt? Some feeble efforts
have gone recently into the building of some
recently founded universities, as for example in
Britain. No one of them has involved the planning effort which was put into Kings College
Chapel at Cambridge, nor indeed so much as
went into a single doorway of that Chapel. All
these modern classrooms and offices are built
rather on the assumption that the institution
will not be wanted for as much as a hundred

years and that, even if wanted, it will not be there. Modern pictures are painted on the same principle, the artist sparing a day to complete a canvas which may be expected to last a decade. The rebuilt Coventry Cathedral is thus the dying image of impermanence, one in which one senses that a greater effort was beyond the energy of all concerned.

What is true of buildings or pictures is true again, of the individual. The aristocratic principle assumes an assured future in a stable community. The acquiring of property and the planting of trees is paralleled by the breeding and training of the next generation. In such a society individuals may grow up with a sense of purpose, with work to be done, with responsibilities to be assumed, with ancestors to inspire and descendants to admonish. A firmly established society allows of a long-term strategy, with further goals to be attained by successive generations. Individual decadence begins when that sense of purpose is lost. People are said to be decadent when they have nothing to do but gamble and drink and go to the races. Still lower depths of decadence are reached when men are effeminate, when women are faithless, when children are neglected, when drugs are in vogue. Oscar Wilde typified the self-conscious decadence of London in 1890-1900, and Saki (H. H. Munro) portrayed the more advanced decadence of 1900-1914. The point is not that a few people behaved badly but that a whole generation had lost its sense of direction. At a fairly defined moment in history the British momentum had been spent.

Throughout history civilisations and empires have reached the same point, their decline becoming apparent (at least in retrospect) and we do well to study the process from every angle. The ultimate causes may be obscure but the various stages followed a pattern which would seem to be all but inevitable.

The first stage on the downward path is one of over-centralisation. Everything is done to eliminate or neutralise all but the main and central seat of administration. The lesser centres of power are either provincial governments or organisations which can be classified as religious, financial, military or economic: an archbishopric, a national bank, a military command or a major industrial or trading group. The attempt to centralise all power in the one capital city and, indeed in its administrative quarter, means the assimilation of all possible rival institutions from monasteries to television studios, from harbour authorities to charitable foundations. All these can be eliminated in the name of democracy or efficiency, and the result is the creation of the one government machine into which all problems are fed and from which all wisdom is to emerge. All that is initially lost is the likelihood of the government's having to listen to informed criticism from outside its inner circle of officials. Thereafter the problems centre upon the growing size and complexity of the central administration. As the civil servants multiply there is an ever increasing distance between the citizen and the nameless people who will ultimately decide upon his application, protest or appeal. Proceedings are cumbrous and attitudes are hierarchical, all decisions being referred from the periphery to the centre and then from the bottom to the top. "If death came from Madrid," said sixteenth century Spaniards, "we should all live to a very great age."

Much the same comment must have been made about Babylon, Peking, Persepolis, Delhi and London. Less frequently noticed are two other results of over-centralisation. The first is that the normal processes of retirement and promotion will bring to the centre the people who have been robbed of all initiative while posted at the circumference. The second is that the capital city is now appallingly vulnerable to internal sedition or external assault. When all roads lead to Rome, all cables to London, the usual channels to Paris, the whole administrative machine can be taken over by an infantry brigade or can be knocked out by a single rocket attack. There are no centres of authority outside the target area, no alternative capital city to which a government might move. With the capital city gone, there is nothing left.

The second stage in the process of decline and fall is represented by the growth of taxation.Taxes become heavier in time of war and should diminish, by rights, when the war is over. That is not, however, what happens. Although sometimes lowered when war ends, taxes seldom regain their pre-war level. That is because the level of expenditure rises to meet the war-time level of taxation. It has been too widely assumed that increased expenditure leads to heavier taxation. The fact is, however, that it is the taxes which cause the expenditure. The result is that each war represents another step on the ascending staircase of taxation. Up to a certain point taxation is regarded as an inevitable and unavoidable nuisance. It was thus assumed in ancient China that one-tenth of the produce should be ample to meet all the government expenses, and this was accepted as perfectly just and equitable. To taxation on this scale peoples elsewhere were more or less resigned. The story of taxation is long and complicated but the central fact was stated by Gladstone in 1858:

I believe that it [the income tax] does more than any other tax to demoralise and corrupt the people . . . So long as you consent, without a special purpose, to levy the in-

*come tax as a fact of the ordinary and per-
manent revenue of the country, so long will
it be vain to talk of economy and effective
reduction of expenditure.*

All subsequent experience has tended to prove
his point and the growth of administrative
machinery has made it possible to impose
higher levels of taxation than would formerly
have been thought possible.

Our present concern is not with fiscal
burdens as such but with over-taxation as an
aspect of decay. It was an important factor in
the collapse of the Roman Empire, many of the
provinces having been bled white before any external threat developed. It certainly played a
big part in the decline and fall of Mogul India,
the Muslims having taxed the Hindus to the
point at which trade dwindled and large areas
of land went out of cultivation. In more modern
times a high rate of taxation did much to ruin
Spain, the government of which was virtually
bankrupt by 1693. The Dutch Republic was
similarly ruined by the taxation which accompanied the War of the Spanish Succession. As
for the French Revolution, it took place at a moment, following the War of American Independence, when taxation took from 38 to 41
percent of the taxpayers' income. It had
reached a point moreover when no further tax
could have produced any higher revenue, it be-

ing recognised that the expenses of collection would exceed the value of the sums collected.

In much the same way many of the countries of Western Europe in the twentieth century are approaching or have reached a point at which all organised government must break down for lack of funds. Taxation on this scale must perhaps be considered a symptom rather than a cause of decay. What is essential to realise, however, is that the taxation causes the expenditure and the expenditure is an evil in itself, not merely a waste of money. For government expenditure is the chief cause of inflation and is also the means of government interference in commercial, industrial, and social life. Where evil has been averted it has been normally from lack of funds. Where evil has been done it was usually because the perpetrators had money to spend. Taxation, taken to the limit and beyond, has always been a sign of decadence and a prelude to disaster.

The third stage in the process of decline and fall is the growth of a top-heavy system of administration. Much could be said on this subject, but it may be sufficient to indicate three areas of decay. First of all, there is a widening chasm between the government and the governed. The central administration is remote from the individual, the capital city being distant, the high officials nameless and aloof, all correspondence being dilatory and no problem (other than the payment of taxes) being regarded as urgent. It is not "our" government but a great characterless machine, swallowing money and churning out paper. We have no interest in its activities but seek only to avoid its notice and keep out of its way. Any large organisation, as we know from our own experience, has a life of its own and lives only for itself. Members of a legislature, the supposed guardians of our welfare, live in a little world of their own, sharing a technical language, having their own gossip, smiling at their own humour and basing their own plans on the assumptions they have in common. They have little or no connection with the world at large and their permanent officials have, if anything, less. Those who are theoretically men of power have surprisingly little real authority, being caught up in a machine which moves slowly in some unintended direction. If there were a steering wheel — and none is visible — the machine would not respond to it. The way things are going was settled long ago and nothing we say or do will make any difference.

The fourth stage is represented by the promotion of the wrong people. Men and women begin their official career at a low level in the administrative pyramid. They find at the outset that conformity is the key to success. In an army or navy at war, even perhaps in a foreign service, there will be moments of crisis in which the best men will assume the lead and in which the bogus will be found out. The same cannot be said of a ministry of agriculture and fisheries, nor indeed of a ministry of pensions. There are, in fact, many areas of administration in which nothing much is going to happen. Seniors will retire when they reach the retiring age and those next in seniority will succeed them. Those who have most closely patterned themselves on their elders are the men who will obtain promotion. And how can it be otherwise? There is no standard of achievement by which people can be judged. To have carried out routine duties correctly is all that is asked. To improve on procedures is more than is wanted. To have original ideas would be a bar to success. This situation is probably inevitable and eternal but the same tendency, in a decadent society, rubs off on other people. A tame conformity becomes the characteristic of people in banking and industry, in journalism and law. The whole society, as well as the whole organisation, becomes lethargic and cumbersome, routine-ridden and tame. All have discovered the secret that mistakes are best avoided by doing nothing at all. When there is an emergency, therefore, the immediate effect is mere panic. No decision will be made by folk who have never had to make a decision. No prompt and sensible orders will come from people who have known only routine.

In the big organisation the wrong men are promoted and wrong men tend to reach wrong decisions. This is especially probable in the sort of department where A makes a recommendation to B, who makes a different recommendation on the minute sheet before passing the file to C, who revises the wording and sends the file on to D, who goes back to an improved version of A's minute and so lays the file before E, who lays it in turn before F for signature. With successive scrutiny by so many of the wise and good, the final version should be an impressive document embodying all the wisdom of the ages. But is it and does it? The trouble is that A, foreseeing all the changes that will be made by officials B to E takes very little trouble over the first minute on the file. Indeed, the more he sees his work mangled the less attention he pays to the next document under discussion. He says "yes" and "no" at random or alternately. But the time will come when officials B, C, and D are all preoccupied with something more important. On this occasion they agree hastily with all that is put before them. But E has come to rely on their experience and judgment. Assuming that they have done the work, he initials the file and lays it before F, whose trust in E is absolute. So F signs the document which thus comes to represent the government's decision. It is, actually, however, A's decision, taken more or less at random, each of the other officials believing that the work has been done by someone else. It is the sad fact that any one of them would have done better by himself, giving more thought to it than he will ever do while sharing the responsibility with others.

The fifth stage on the downward path is represented by the urge to overspend. Governments have always tended to spend more than they have, and the urge is stronger now than ever before. Here the basic mistake lies in the compiling and presentation of estimates. Each government department is invited to outline its needs for the coming year. The officials concerned take the figure for the present year, add to it the cost of the additions and improvements they have in mind, add ten percent to that — so as to allow room for concessions to the treasury — and submit the grand total as their estimate. When all the departments have been through this process, their several estimates are considered by the treasury and the cabinet, possibly queried and discussed, perhaps fractionally reduced, and then finally added up. This figure is then presented to the legislature and governs the amount which is at last demanded in tax. That is the sequence of events and it is totally wrong. The whole calculation should have begun at the other end. The first step should have been for the legislature to decide what proportion of the gross national product should go to the government and how that amount should be raised. The second step should have been to translate that into a total sum. The third step should have been to divide that sum between the ministries, giving each one a maximum figure which it must not exceed. Towards achieving any sort of economy in public affairs the adoption of that procedure would at least be a beginning. But that is not what we do. We add up estimates instead of dividing a fixed sum, and the result is a consistent pattern of deficit. It is this deficit that is the cause of inflation, and it is inflation which destroys the middle classes upon which the government must rely for its military strength and its balance of trade. By this system of estimates and deficits the modern government quite literally blows out its brains.

The roots of departmental overspending are all too easy to follow. By widening the scope of his activity the official adds to his own consequence. His status within the organisation is related to the number of his subordinates. To assume new responsibilities will make him popular among his followers, giving him the chance to promote those whose loyalty has been most eloquently expressed. By the same measures he will have the chance to frustrate rivals who might have assumed the same responsibilities had they thought of it in time. With more money to be spent go higher honours and higher salary together with a greater sense of achievement. In an expanding organisation all can look to a bright future of bustling activity and public notice. And, apart from that, the rising expenditures can always be justified. All our hospitals are obsolete and should be replaced. All our primary schools should be made to look like secondary schools. All our prisons need to be enlarged as new laws create new offences. More financial aid should be given to the more obviously hostile African tribes. More unsuitable students should be admitted to more disorganised universities. There are as many good ways of spending money as there are civil servants, and each new way will add again to the cost of administration. So the minister is under pressure from below, being assured that the estimates represent the very minimum required. In so far, moreover, as the Treasury interferes, its activity is definitely harmful. So the final result is that each ministry demands more money each year, and the total required by government is correspondingly, dramatically and eternally increased.

Whether supposedly democratic or openly dictatorial, governments have to seek a measure of acquiescence and support. The ministers know that welfare measures are popular and that taxes are unwelcome. So the ideal government programme involves added expenditure and reduced revenue and this implies a deficit. Among individuals and commercial firms that would be the road to bankruptcy, but governments have open to them the alternative policy of inflation. They make good the annual deficit by printing more banknotes and allowing the banks to extend more credit. The situation is saved and the value of the currency is reduced by the amount of the deficit. This simple but ingenious plan has certain other advantages. All the sums which the government has borrowed — at any rate from its own citizens — are to some extent cancelled. All the promises it had made are in some measure reduced in value. All the pay raises it has been forced to concede are to that extent illusory. In effect the government goes bankrupt and pays out only a proportion of its debts. We avoid the word bankruptcy, however, and the government is allowed to continue its tottering and discredited existence. In order to shuffle somehow through the shameful present, it has cheated its creditors and mortgaged the future. Lacking the courage to reduce its expenditure, lacking the means of improving the revenue (the taxes having hit the ceiling), the government incurs a vast debt and loads it on the shoulders of some future generation. That is what we mean by inflation, and any individual who followed the government's example would undoubtedly go to prison as a fraudulent bankrupt.

Why do ministers behave in this way? They are, many of them, men of average ability and fair education, men with some business experience and some knowledge of economics. More than that, they are often model householders, husbands and fathers, accustomed to paying their bills, capable of understanding a balance sheet and confident of maintaining a credit balance in their current account. They are most of them incapable of cheating a tradesman or leaving a hotel with their account unsettled. How can men supposedly honest in their private transactions prove so consistently fraudulent in public life? It cannot be for lack of information, for warnings have come repeatedly from bankers and economists. Here, for example, are two extracts from reports published by the American Institute for Economic Research, reports which are available to anyone:

> This *"borrowing"* of previously non-existent purchasing media is only a portion of the total Federal debt of about $470 billion. The roughly $130 billion held by private nonbank investors reflect past expenditure by the Federal Government of already-existing purchasing media.
>
> The deficits of the Federal budget, whether financed with inflationary or noninflationary purchasing media, have made the Federal Government the largest

debtors in the Nation and the World. As such the Federal Government has benefited to the extent that its eventual repayments, if any, will represent far less real wealth than did the purchasing media originally borrowed.

Research Report
April 15, 1974

But deficit finance has not been confined to U.S.A. as this Investment Bulletin makes clear:

The consequence of nearly 4 decades of almost continuous inflating are becoming more evident with each successive international monetary crisis. All now have lost about two-thirds, at least, of their pre-World War II buying power, and all seem destined to depreciate much more in the next several years, perhaps for as long as a few decades before they become practically worthless . . .

Politicians generally insist on remaining in their Politicians' Paradise where lavish promises in order to obtain votes are fulfilled with inflationary purchasing media created to finance government deficits. Their accomplices in embezzling the savings and life insurances of the people of Western civilisation are the central bankers of the leading nations. Without exception they choose to remain in their

Bankers' Heaven where promises to pay are, as John Exter pointed out, simply "I owe you nothing" and the people of Western civilisation are beginning to endure the Hell that has been paved with the good intentions of those who would save the world (and incidentally retain power, or is it vice versa) by the money-credit manipulation.

We see little possibility that there will be a return to sound money-credit procedure until after some bitter lessons have been learned.

American Institute for Economic Research Bulletin Vol. XLI, No. 8

But why should politicians cling to their Politicians' Paradise? Can they not sense the disasters towards which they are heading? Can they not recognise a collision course when they see it? Do they not perceive what the future holds for them and for us? The answer is that there is no future. Without any conscious thought they have come to the conclusion that the interests of the next generation can be and should be ignored. The collapse will have come before anyone can foreclose on their mortgages. The world of the year 2000 must take care of itself. It will not be the world we know today. This is not what any politician will say in so many words. It is what is implicit in all that they do, and it is this rejection of the future which is the very essence of decay. All over the world there are hopeful young people planning a career for their children. They are perhaps a minority among parents but they still exist. They pay heavily for an education which the State has now ceased to provide. They improve property and plant trees. They scheme to leave behind them an estate, a name for honest dealing, a tradition of private benefaction and of public service. There can be no certainty about the future but of one thing we can be sure. These young peoples' dreams are not shared by those who are to be seen in the corridors of power. They at least are without illusion or hope. For them the game is already lost, the plans cancelled and the books closed.

The sixth symptom of decadence is what we call liberal opinion. This is an attitude of mind rather than anything we associate with a political party. It is common to a multitude of well-meaning people whose ideas are broadly benevolent and progressive. They have three recognisable characteristics. The first is that their views are based upon a sense of highly moral but unstated and unproven assumptions. The second is that they are savagely intolerant of any views which differ from theirs. The third is that they are always remote from the arena to which their high-minded principles are meant to apply. In more precise terms they see no objection, in the abstract, to the marriage of a white girl to a black and feel that nothing should be done to discourage it. Anyone who urges the girl to think again about it is a narrow-minded fascist who deserves to be driven out of all decent society. But they themselves, as it happens, are not resident in New York or Wolverhampton nor even in Notting Hill and are so placed (unluckily) that their daughter never meets any blacks at all. Their spiritual ancestors were the New Englanders who demanded the emancipation of blacks in the deep South but took a slightly different view when the blacks came to Boston. The point here is not that the "do-gooder's" opinion is necessarily wrong — for there is much to be said, no doubt, on either side — but that they shower abuse on anyone whose opinion differs from theirs, subsequently revealing that their own ethical standards are meant only to apply to other people. That is the liberal viewpoint as upheld in the newspapers, radio, television and politics. It involves a set of beliefs — one, for example, being a belief in the wickedness of all white South Africans — which we doubt at our peril. We can be pilloried, ostracised, silenced and even prosecuted for upholding any view on this matter that is not accepted as orthodox.

What concerns our argument is not that the world's do-gooders are mistaken but that their attitude is decadent. They are moved by sentiment rather than by reason and that is itself a symptom of decay. Still more to the point, their interest is solely in the present and for them, too, the future is merely the end. This is well illustrated by the liberal attitude towards foreign aid. Anyone who questions that policy of paying subsidies (as the Romans did) to more or less barbarian tribes is obviously a mean and illiberal reactionary. But the question is still asked whether payments of this sort are really beneficial to the tribes concerned. Are they not destructive of the economy they are meant to save? Should not these backward people be encouraged to plan their own future? Merely to ask those questions is to stir up a hornets' nest. For the liberal dispensers of foreign aid — the money which the donors very often do not even possess and have therefore borrowed — are not concerned with the future of the recipient countries. It is obvious that neither they nor the charity-givers have any future worth considering. The largesse is not for the recipients but is intended for the mental comfort of the donors. They feel that a subscription in this form will justify them in turning away from the problems of Asia and Africa and concentrating once more on their own affairs. A casual payment has ended the matter so far as they are concerned. But the sufferings they have chosen to alleviate are to be lessened more by brains than by charity. If there is anything to be done about Calcutta (a doubtful point) it will not take the form of a shipment of powdered milk.

A study of liberal attitudes would bring out clearly the sharp distinction which exists between sentimentality and sense. It is not to the present purpose to condemn the liberals of the world for their sentimental attitudes towards distant slums, pampered convicts or rioting students. It is true that their typical aim of containing communism led the people of the United States into the Vietnam campaign and an inglorious defeat due mainly to an initial failure to decide what exactly they were trying to do. It is true that a benevolent foreign policy is more of a danger than a policy guided by self-interest — if only because it is unpredictable — but that is not the point. Liberalism is described here merely because it is a symptom of decadence. Even if it were wholly admirable in its genesis and its results, it would still be associated in our minds with periods of decay. We have watched the process by which the British Commonwealth has floundered in a morass of sentimentality. We know something of the lofty ideals which led India from socialism to a temporary dictatorship. Communities with any real vitality do not talk like that nor act like that.

The hallmark of liberal sentimentality lies above all perhaps in a certain attitude towards an agreement or bargain or indeed towards the rule of law. Liberal opinion in India, backed by liberal opinion in Britain, concluded that the Indian princes should lose their territories and estates and even the pensions by which they had been compensated when they ceased to rule. How could their wealth be justified when a million people were starving? How could feudal privileges be justified in the twentieth century? There were a host of arguments against allowing the princes to retain their property. On the other side there was only one argument but it was decisive. Treaties had been signed and sealed by which their rights had been defined and confirmed. It could be argued that these agreements had been too generous. They may have been and it would be hard now to say whether they were or not, but the fault, if there was one, lay in the politicians who accepted the treaties. If the arrangements were unjust they should have not been agreed. But all that is beside the point. Wise or foolish, over-generous or just, the treaties had been signed and the bargains had been made. It remained for the government of India to honour its word. It did nothing of the kind, defending its policy in liberal terms. The significance of this betrayal lies not in the immediate injustice but in the light it sheds on the government concerned. Members of the Congress Party might be filled with the loftiest ideals and the most liberal sentiments but they were, it seemed, unreliable and corrupt.

Would it be fair to say that liberal opinion is always more or less corrupt? It would not be fair. We should be right, however, in saying that the loftiest sentiments are usually the prelude to the ugliest sequel. When we hear of policies which are fair and compassionate we may well suspect that somebody is about to be swindled. Of greater importance, however, is the fact that decadence of the community is well advanced. For liberal and democratic sentiment leads in the end to socialism, the next but not the last, stage in a country's decline and fall. Our present concern is not with criticism or defence, not with praise or blame, but solely with an analysis of decadence. We can recognise decadence, we have found, from its successive symptoms: over-centralisation, excessive taxation, bureaucracy, inflation and the growth of liberal influence. Of these successive symptoms one of the most significant is that of bureaucracy and this is important enough to deserve a chapter to itself.

CHAPTER 4

Bureaucracy

Democracy is a form of government in which a substantial number of the people have some part to play. The number so involved is seldom, in fact, a majority, but the government policy does reflect what many people want, the most clamorous demand being for a redistribution of wealth. Acting on this popular mandate, the government will legislate so as to take money from the more prosperous citizens and give it to the voters who have been least successful in providing for themselves. This type of enactment is not, however, the immediate result of establishing a democracy. It may take several generations for people to rid themselves of old and outdated ideas about property, inheritance, honesty and thrift. The first and obvious step is to demand higher taxes from those best able to pay, the revenue being spent on genuinely public purposes such as architecture, diplomacy and defence. By gradual steps the taxes on wealth become more disproportionate and the expenditure less of an investment, the point being reached when the money exacted from the outvoted but wealthy citizen A is openly distributed between citizens X, Y and Z. The aim is to establish an approximate equality of wealth and that is socialism. Any movement in that direction has two aspects, it should be noted. On the one hand, citizens X, Y and Z are possibly less impoverished, having acquired an unearned income. On the other hand, they may be as poor as ever but more content in that citizen A, as they have been assured, is no longer so prosperous. Politics may thus be based as much on envy as on welfare.

Although the aim of socialism is equality of income, the socialists of the world unite in their belief that this is best achieved by transferring to the State the means of production: the land, the industrial equipment, the capital and raw material. Such a process must certainly undermine the position of the rich or at least the more honest of them, but it is questionable whether it does much for the poor. Its immediate result, in fact, is to establish a vast bureaucracy which is probably more expensive than were the luxury-loving directors who have been displaced. Nor can we doubt that the proliferation of bureaucrats is itself a sign of decadence. Worse even than the expense involved is the system of verbiage and complexity, rigidity and delay. Decisions are not reached until the opportunities have passed. Applications are not considered until the applicant is dead. Realities are replaced by reports and memoranda. The whole process of administration moves more and more slowly until the day comes when it finally grinds to a halt.

The word *bureau* is French and means a writing desk originally covered with *bure*, a coarse woolen cloth. It came to mean an office or a government department, and bureaucracy came to mean government by bureaux or by officials, a government in which authority is divided among numerous offices, all of them adhering to inflexible rules of procedure. We come to think of a bureaucracy as a form of rule in which complex and time-wasting formalities prevent effective action. We come to think of a bureaucrat as one who insists upon a rigid adherence to rules, forms and routine. The word may be French but the form of rule goes back to ancient Egypt and dynastic China. In the modern world bureaucracy is associated, above all, with socialism. Whatever the exact form of rule, however, there are characteristics and certain features by which a government can be identified as bureaucratic. They number six and can be listed as follows: over-centralisation, anonymity, lack of coordination, inflexibility, complexity and incompetence.

Taking these in order, over-centralisation is a basic fault from which the other evils are apt to follow. The most highly centralised countries in the world are Great Britain and France, most other large countries being divided into provinces. Sub-divided in this way are the United States, the Soviet Union, China, India, Canada, Australia, Germany and even the

Netherlands and Switzerland. Once over-centralised, the Republic of South Africa is moving towards a more federal pattern of administration. When he went out of office the late President de Gaulle was trying to do the same for France. Great Britain is moving belatedly in the same direction, with autonomy for Scotland under discussion and autonomy for Wales the possible sequel. In the meanwhile and pending such obviously essential reforms, there are countries which try to administer over fifty million people from a single headquarters. This may be just possible from the technical point of view, but it is a recipe for frustration and the effect of socialism is to make a bad situation worse by widening the scope of government interference.

The most bureaucratic bureaucracy is one in which all official business is concentrated in the one capital city. From the point of view of people in the remote areas, the government is thus remote, something known only by correspondence. It is also to be assumed that the volume of correspondence reaching the same centre from all directions must lead to a congestion of business and an appalling delay over reaching a decision about anything. It is this pressure of work which must, in turn, prevent the high officials from leaving the capital. If the folk in the frontier regions know little about the centre of administration, the folk at the centre know still less about the places they are trying to administer. There inevitably grows up a certain friction between the "armchair critic" and "the man on the spot." There is mounting suspicion that the central administration has no real knowledge of what is going on. On the frontiers people may have to cope with fire and flood, with raging torrents and broken bridges, with plague and pestilence, with espionage and riot. In the capital city the bureaucrats have to deal with nothing but paper. Their concern is with files, not with people or things. The first great bureaucrat in modern Europe was Philip II of Spain and we can trace our filing systems to him. His administration was centralised to the point of lunacy, but it is a question whether he should be an example to follow, or whether we might not take warning from his failure.

The second characteristic of a bureaucratic government is that its appointed officials are impersonal, nameless and faceless. Each clerk writes in the name of the government. There was a time in one author's life when he wrote an occasional letter which began: "Sir, I am commanded by the Army Council to bring the following matter to your attention. . . etc." It was a lie. The Army Council knew nothing about the letter and as little about its author. One may doubt whether the wartime Army Council even met, or would have been interested, had it met, in the subject of the letter.

But the form of words was designed to make the recipient of the letter forget about individuals and think only of a mythical assembly of the great and the good. The letter, conveying the decision, is signed by one officer on behalf of another who is deputy to someone more senior who possibly represents the Queen. The effect on the recipient is daunting because he does not know to whom his reply should be addressed or whether it will be seen by anybody. He concludes that he is addressing a system, not a person and that the officer who signed the letter is not an individual but a small part of a complex machine. It is the essence of a bureaucracy to leave us without any idea as to who the rulers are.

The third characteristic of a bureaucracy is that its officials are divided among departments which are distinct from each other, contrasting in attitude and often mutually hostile. Before you build a house you need planning permission. It is your duty to approach, severally, the planning authority, the district engineer, the water board, the electricity council, the regional architect, the telephone manager and the parish council. Some of these authorities are at war with each other. Others are unaware of each other's existence. When you alter the plans to satisfy the rules administered by the district engineer, you spoil the elevation already approved by the regional architect.

Your drive entrance is acceptable to the highway planners but does not please the parish council. We are all probably familiar with the situation when a water pipe is laid by the water board, the trench being filled in and the surface made good. A month later the road is closed again for the laying of drains, the trench filled in and the surface made good. A month later the road is closed once more by the electricity board, the trench filled in and the surface made good. In many countries all these authorities are distinct, and there is no chance at all of their using the same trench by previous agreement — still less of the road's having a service pipe in which all services might be contained. On the higher level the coordination is probably worse, the welfare department giving a pension to a man who is wanted by the police for burglary, the army enlisting the man who just deserted from the air force, the home department expelling the alien whom the foreign ministry wants to question. We thus think of bureaucracy as a system in which coordination is minimal and ineffective.

The fourth characteristic of a bureaucracy is that the officials are applying inflexible rules which are often opposed to common sense. To give the official wide powers of interpretation in the application of laws, regulations and decrees would expose him, it is thought, to both temptation and personal attack. He might, on the one hand, accept bribes or show favour to his friends and relatives. He could, on the other hand, make enemies, being branded as a tyrant by all who were disappointed in their applications. To safeguard his position we narrowly restrict his powers. All he says is: "Planning permission is refused because your application is contrary to sub-para. 17 of Para. 691, Section 109 of the Act of 1951." He does not say that the proposal put forward is undesirable. He gives no opinion about that. He merely points to a regulation and hides once more in the anonymity of his department. There may seem to be good reasons for giving him this narrow task of interpretation. It is arguably inevitable that he should be put in that position. What is unfortunate is that legal phrases do not cover everything and that strict adherence to the law can be ridiculous or even tragic. We hear of the ambulance racing to hospital with an emergency case, only to be told that the patient cannot be admitted to that hospital but must be taken somewhere else — even when this may mean his death on the way there. "I have no power to make an exception" is the formula used, and this is quite possibly true. We think of bureaucracy as a system under which officials can thus avoid taking any responsibility.

The fifth characteristic of bureaucracy is that the procedures as laid down are apt to be appallingly complex. There are forms to be filled in, rules to be observed, technicalities to be understood and documents to be drawn up. The merchant who has goods to export cannot even pretend to understand the clearances and permits which must accompany the shipment. He hands the task to a forwarding agent who does nothing else. Complexity goes with the size of the organisation but it is also the tendency for complexity to become more complex. One cause of this is the desire of the expert to protect his special knowledge, adding to the mystery rather than attempting to explain. Another cause of this is the overstaffing of the civil service, leading to the creation of work to justify the numbers employed. Any questionnaire or census form will thus become more complicated as time goes on, providing work for the department concerned. Complexity thus becomes in this way more complex, and we can all recognise in this an aspect of bureaucracy.

All these five characteristics come together in the sixth and last, which is incompetence due to a lack of purpose and speed. Carried to its normal conclusion, delay becomes denial, centralisation becomes frustration, departmentalism becomes inaction, inflexibility becomes idleness and complexity becomes decay (Third Law of Parkinson). Slowly and majestically the whole machinery of government grinds to a standstill. Little is attempted, nothing is achieved and even the simplest problems prove insoluble. A good example of this is to be found in the United States where the Constitution was designed for a different kind of society but is so drawn up as to make reform practically impossible. The difficulties into which the American executive, legislature and judiciary have been drawn by the Watergate affair are not due as much to the wickedness of individuals as to the obsolescence of a whole system of government. The framework is weak, the ideas are bad in principle and the bureaucracy is revolting in its complexity. The whole cumbersome machine drifted into an external conflict in Southeast Asia which was futile from the outset and from which it proved almost impossible to withdraw. There have been successive blunders in foreign policy, and the internal problems are endemic and seemingly insoluble. Beyond all these flounderings in the mud stands the central fact that the system is at fault and that the means for changing the system are, for all practical purposes, nonexistent.

These, then, are the six characteristics of bureaucracy. We should, however, bear in mind that bureaucracy is a type of administration, not a form of rule, and can exist wherever the government is highly centralised. It can flourish, therefore, under monarchy, aristocracy, democracy or dictatorship. It is widely supposed in Western Europe that elective democracy is the best form of rule. This is a doubtful proposition at best, but allowing it to be the fact, we should still have to recognise that democracy is quite consistent with bureaucracy and that democratic equality gives strength to the bureaucrat. It is also apparent that bureaucracy is worse in the large countries, distance being an important factor in substituting correspondence for conversation. As against that, we can ignore for the present the subject of corruption. It can exist under any form of rule and in any size country. It can be an aspect of bureaucracy, but there is nothing invariable about that. The evils of bureaucracy are as serious, however, when the officials are honest, but stupid, as when they accept bribes — indeed, they are possibly worse. Let us assume, nevertheless, that the government itself is more or less democratic and well-meaning, that the country is highly centralised and that there is no more corruption than might be regarded as normal in any society. The problem we have to face is that of bureaucracy, and our task is to decide what we are to do about it.

It would be logical at this point to remind ourselves again of the aspects of bureaucracy we have already listed: centralisation, impersonality, departmentalism, rigidity, complexity, and finally, incompetence. These are the evils for which we have to find a remedy, replacing them by delegation, responsibility, coordination, flexibility, simplicity and effectiveness. Basis for all that follows is decentralisation. There is in every country a system of local and regional government, but the trend, and especially the socialist trend, is to make each of the local and provincial governments nothing more than an agency for the central government. The opposite or anti-bureaucratic movement would be to take whole areas of administration and make them a purely local matter in which the central government has no say whatever. It is arguable that all the disputes about what we call socialism should be purely regional. Welfare, housing, health and education should never come before the central government at all. There can be and there should be wide differences between one province and another, the more valuable in that the results can be compared. From the point of view of bureaucracy the great advantage of decentralisation is to bring the official within reach. He is there to be questioned and we can meet him in the street. He ceases to be nameless and faceless. He begins to be responsible.

Another possible reform would be to halve the numbers of the civil servants and, in some instances, double their pay. There is a big difference in the armed forces between the sergeant who says, "It has always been done this way" and the officer who says, "It would be quicker to do it like this." We cumber our offices with clerks of the sergeant mentality and have too few men of the officer type. British administration was at its best in India and the Sudan and at its worst in Britain. The whole of Malaya used to be administered by two hundred men, all of them ready to assume responsibility, all of them able to make a decision. India, a sub-continent, used to be ruled by the Indian Civil Service, numbering about a thousand to twelve hundred at the time when India became independent in 1947. Reduce the total number and you have fewer steps between the foot and the summit of the pyramid. This means obtaining a quicker decision at lower cost — it may even be a wiser decision and certainly should not be worse. Given a smaller service you will have more personalities and fewer rules.

There is also much to be said for reorganising the departments (or some of them) so that they correspond to social needs rather than departmental convenience. Until very recently hospitals in Britain were organised purely for the convenience of medical specialists. One ward was for the patients with ear, nose and throat complaints, another for patients with chest ailments. This meant that one specialist, with pupils at heel, could go quickly from case to case. All this has now been changed for the better, the new arrangement being for the convenience of the nurses. We now classify patients according to the seriousness of their illness, all those very ill being placed (whatever their illness) in an intensive care ward, all those mildly indisposed to a different ward, and so on. This makes it possible to concentrate the best nurses on the more serious cases, putting the inexperienced nurses on the wards where they can't do much harm and where the patients can help to look after each other. This is a real improvement and might even lead, some day, to our planning a hospital for the patients' convenience (a still more revolutionary idea). Now apply the same principle to the process of obtaining planning permission to build a house. In many countries we should need to approach the following authorities, each represented by an official backed by a committee:

> Local Council (Housing)
> Planning Authority (Highways)
> District Engineer (Public Works
>   Dept., Drainage etc. . .)
> Architect (Amenities Committee)
> Water Board
> Electricity Board
> Telephone Council

The list varies and it could be longer. Were we restoring an old house, by the way, we should also be faced by the Archaeological

Committee. (The worst disaster of all is to find a Roman temple under the top soil.) So we may have to deal with seven or eight committees in all. The obvious reform is to abolish all the committees, replacing each by one man. Then collect those seven or eight men into a new committee on HOUSING, with just one official to deal with each applicant. Our task is now to approach just the one official, who says, "You can build a house on the site marked, but there will be no main drainage for five years and no telephone in the immediate future." How can one man, you ask, have knowledge enough to cover all those aspects? There is, in fact, no real difficulty about it. And if the one official says no, we can then appeal to the committee. It is only appeals, moreover, that the committee will have to consider.

Another possible reform concerns the action open to us when we fail to obtain a sensible answer. First of all, we must outlaw the official postcard acknowledging receipt of our application or letter and assuring us that the matter is receiving attention. This is, of course, a lie. It is not receiving attention. If it were, the reply would be in a more intelligent form. What we must hasten is the actual response, remembering that it will take just as long to write it in a month's time as it will today. The delay in replying is not due to solemn discussion about the point at issue but simply to overstaffing and to bad organisation of the work. Now, our remedy for all this delay lies, in theory, in the democratic process. The permanent official is supposed to be controlled by the elected representative. It is a question, however, whether this is true or whether the minister is controlled by the officials. There may be no simple answer to this, but one can think of a better system than an ombudsman or a question in Parliament. One way would be to make real and practical use of television and radio. There should be question time each evening at the same hour. "Why have I not received an answer to my letter of such-a-date?" And the department would be invited to reply. We are wasting television time in so-called entertainment and throwing away our chance of putting it to some practical use. It should give us our chance to put the procrastinating official into the witness box or indeed the pillory. For civil servants a possible policy would be to halve their numbers, double their pay and then demand results.

There is a case, we have seen, for decentralisation, for the delegation of powers to the provinces. It is arguable that this would lead to an improved administration, especially at the level of public contact. There would be, however, another and even more important result. If the central government were relieved of all responsibility for matters of merely local concern, it would have time to consider at length and at leisure the matters which are truly of national concern. Most national legislatures are appallingly over-worked and quite unable to deal properly with the business they are supposed to transact. While there seems to be time for a fair amount of nonsense, there are matters deferred from one session to another and hasty decisions taken on matters which have hardly been discussed. Over-centralisation has certain advantages for certain purposes. It is essential for example to an aggressive foreign policy or to the conquest of an empire. It brings with it, however, as its inevitable result, a congestion of business at the centre. This is a disease from which many present day governments are suffering and with serious results. There is a current and growing revolt against the present type of democratic and more or less socialist government. They are mostly unworkable, and even when temporarily workable, they are a bore. Our need is for something which corresponds to the technology of the age in which we live. But all our political systems reflect rather the age of the horse-drawn vehicle.

Perhaps the most extraordinary feature of the present age is the contrast between the rapid progress made in technology and the stagnation of thought about politics. Indeed, the word *stagnation* is an understatement because we seem to have forgotten all the principles we ever learnt. One of the first, for example, recited at kindergarten level, is this: "Never pay blackmail to anyone," a rule now broken almost daily. So the outlook is more than uncertain and we are driven to seek remedies for our present ills. Some possible remedies have already been discussed, more of them involving no more than a simple reorganisation. But the question arises: will anything be done? And we realise in asking the question, that we are faced by an appalling deadweight of inertia. There are vested interests, as we know, and there are all sorts of minor dishonesties, but the real obstacle is sheer idleness.

Even when they know what has to be done the politicians and civil servants lack the energy to do it. For one reason or another the time is not ripe. It is too soon after the last general election or there is too little time before the next. For a host of excellent reasons nothing can be done at the present time. The time for action is never now. Bureaucracy can exist under any form of rule but some people suppose that it is more tolerable in a democracy. There is no certainty about this and some reasons for thinking that democracy makes it worse. For one thing, it may well add to the delay. The council meets only once a month and the agenda for next month is already complete. The committee has now referred the matter to a sub-committee. There is to be a commission of inquiry. The legislature's session will end next week and there was no time to deal with this matter, which will be raised again in the autumn. The matter did come before the legislature, but there was no quorum present and the proposal accordingly lapsed. For another thing, the scheme, whatever it is, can be so mangled in committee and sub-committee that the decision finally reached is meaningless. There is a final risk that argument will continue until the originators of the proposal are themselves tired of the whole thing and ready to give up. In other words, bureaucracy does not readily yield to any democratic process. It is more likely to bring democracy into disrepute, hastening the process by which the rule of the people turns into the rule of the mob. The answer to the inefficiencies of bureaucracy would be a strong and ruthless reforming government, but is this the sort of government we are likely to elect?

Amidst many uncertainties, the one thing clear is that the key to success lies in the energy of the individual. We have men enough who will cope with the daily tasks of administration, emptying the in-tray by evening and leaving the office late after another day of bureaucratic toil. What we need, however, is men who will do that and still have energy left to ask whether all the paperwork is really necessary. More than that, we want the men and women who will complete what is now the normal career and have years left in which to reorganise and simplify the present procedures. If we could live to a hundred, say, with undiminished vigour until we should reach the age of ninety, we might have people aged eighty with more experience than we now have at the age of retirement and with more energy than many now have at the age of fifty. If we are to check our civilisation's present decline, it must be through some such change in our pattern of life. That should be our immediate aim. We should not, however, by achieving it reach any Utopia or return to any Golden Age. We make too many mistakes at the best of times. That we could reverse the present decline is most improbable, but it would be more than worthwhile to slow it down.

Reform of our institutions would be valuable but the changes most needed are in ourselves. To abolish a thousand committees might be useful in itself, provided that each were replaced by an individual. But greater advantage would derive from appointing individuals who would combine experience with dynamic energy, tact with integrity, imagination with a sense of reality. It is the purpose of this book to argue that such men could be brought into existence, partly no doubt by education and improved selection procedures, but mainly by improvements in diet and by taking enough vitamins. We should not claim that all is known about diet that needs to be known.

We do not suppose that the answer to our problem is simple and obvious. What we do maintain is that research in this area might yield some vitally important results. Failing such discoveries, we must follow the treadmill round from democracy and bureaucracy to mob rule and chaos and so come to live under the dictatorship which those evils must bring about.

CHAPTER 5

Dictatorship

The well-meaning, liberal socialist, mildly corrupt and democratically elected government will normally prepare the way for its own overthrow. The process is more or less inevitable, and examples have multiplied since the present century began. The history of the *coup d'état,* as opposed to the revolution, has been made the subject of a detailed study by Edward Luttwak (*Coup d'État, A Practical Handbook,* Penguin Books, 1968). Luttwak lists eighty-four attempted *coups d'état* between 1946 and 1964, fifty-three of them being successful. Of this grand total Latin America provided forty-five examples, eleven of them successful; Asia, some seventeen examples, eleven of them successful; the Middle East, twelve examples, nine successful; and Africa ten examples, four of them successful. There have been many *coups d'état* since 1964 — nine of them for instance, since 1966 — so there is no real shortage of material for study. Many of these recorded successes and failures took place in relatively uncivilised countries, but we can draw conclusions from the list which apply to the world in general. The first and obvious conclusion is that the *coup d'état* is normally caused by the weakness of the government in power. Rarely is any attempt made against a strong and ruthless government, well-entrenched and tenacious of power. That the *coup d'état* should be attempted is usually a sign that the government is wavering and vulnerable. Our present concern, however, is not with all governments but only with those which were more or less democratic and which have become more or less dictatorial. There are enough of these to provide the material from which certain conclusions may be drawn.

The first step towards self-destruction has been described in the last chapter. It involves setting up a bureaucracy which tends to prevent communication between the government and the people. Those in power become ever more remote, being approached only through "the usual channels." This sort of remoteness must become more apparent when there are frequent changes in government, with regroupings and coalitions. In that event ministers are too transient to have much influence on their ministries and have too little time to establish their reputation with the public. It is apparent, on the other hand, that the senior civil servants have no special loyalty to any one government and are prepared to carry on as before after the *coup d'état* has taken place. The more impersonal the machinery of administration, the less actual support will it provide for any elected ministry.

There was a time when elected politicians had to remain in fairly close contact with writers and journalists, landowners and industrialists, but it is now easy for them to avoid all such direct sounding of public opinion. They can rely, if they wish, on the bureaucracy for that and for everything else. But the bureaucracy may do little to identify the first signs of revolt. It may not itself be threatened, and it may be indifferent to the political changes which might ensue. The more monolithic the structure, the less will it do for the party in power.

The second step towards self-destruction is to centralise all power in the capital city. If the trend of democracy is towards socialism, the trend of socialism is towards over-centralisation. All must be done to reduce the power of the monarchy, the church, the nobility, the monasteries, the banks, the universities, the schools, the foundations and the charities. All must be brought under governmental control in the name of democracy, each provincial and city government becoming a mere agency for carrying out the party programme. Following on the general policy of centralisation, all police must be made subordinates of the central government, it being plainly absurd that police activities should be hampered by a network of internal boundaries. There are all sorts of good reasons for centralisation, some of them cen-tred upon administrative convenience and the usefulness of standardised procedure, some of them concerned with equality and others fairly directed against any measure of local autonomy. The final result is to centre all power in the ministries, leaving little beyond their control and nothing beyond their influence. There is, moreover, a further tendency to increase the power of the prime minister at the expense of his colleagues. Over-centralisation goes with bureaucracy and becomes more complete with the passage of time.

Under a socialist regime the urge to over-centralise is extended to industry and commerce. With all else brought under bureaucratic control, it is an absurd anomaly that leaders of industry should be allowed to do as they like. What right have they to control great financial and commercial undertakings? Who are they to decide upon wages and prices and hours of work? They are gradually brought to heel, being controlled by legislation and advised by government. Selected institutions are nationalised; companies short of capital are bought out; companies are compelled to amalgamate in the name of efficiency; others are warned against amalgamation so as not to create a monopoly. Step by step the more important industries are brought under indirect control. Companies seeking to expand are induced to set up industrial plants in areas where there is unemployment and where industrial unrest is endemic. Other companies are controlled by the allocation of government contracts or the direction of subsidies and grants. The immediate aim is for governments to gain a controlling interest in every major firm or group, ensuring that all decisions are finalised by the appropriate ministry. The final aim is to nationalise all industry and commerce, enlisting all business men into a new type of civil service under direct government control. With the economic consequences of this policy we are not immediately concerned. Of more present significance is the fact that all activities are now controlled from the capital city. All lines of communication lead back to the ministries, all problems are to be decided in the cabinet. The policy of over-centralisation has been carried to its logical extreme.

Should we protest at this concentration of power we shall be reminded that the country is still a democracy, that ministers are responsible to the legislature and that elected representatives are responsible to their constituents. So they are and we do well to remember the fact. But the actual force of public opinion produces some rather unfortunate results. This brings us to the government's third step towards self-destruction, the step we call inflation. Each political party gains office by offering the electorate what it is supposed to want. Careful market research has established that voters agree in wanting improved social benefits coupled with reduced taxation.

To gain and keep the approval of the majority, the ministers must provide free hospitals, free schools, free universities, free meals, free entertainment and generous pensions. It was originally and hopefully assumed that these benefits could derive from taxing the rich, but it was eventually discovered that half of the rich were no longer rich and the other half were no longer there. Yet the promise remained to provide more and tax less, which is arithmetically impossible. To fulfil this promise, however, the treasury can resort to inflation. Each year the revenue will be overspent, the deficit being made good by printing more money and allowing more credit. In this way the currency loses its value each year by at least the total sum of the counterfeit notes. When we hear of a government policy proposing to limit inflation to a mere annual ten percent, this means that it is content to see its banknotes worthless by the end of a decade. The government which has caused the inflation is apt to put the blame on workmen who make excessive wage demands. Be that, however, as it may, the central fact is clear that government overspending has caused the disaster with which the country is faced. What the government does with impunity would be enough to earn the individual who did it a jail sentence for fraud. Of all the taxes heaped on the unfortunate citizen, the heaviest is this system of inflation, the tax which falls most heavily on those who have tried to save.

The whole socialist system imposes tremendous strain on the community, encouraging envy and building up resentment. Its more immediate result is to ruin the middle class, leaving bitterness among small investors whose savings have been virtually confiscated and driving small shopkeepers out of business. There builds up a body of citizens with a growing hatred of the party in office and a scarcely less intense hatred of the parties in opposition. The democratic process should offer the voter the opportunity to vote against all the candidates at an election. It does not, and the ruined citizen has thus no legal means of expressing his opinion.

The classic example of a ruined middle class is that of Germany in 1923, and the Weimar Republic is the classic instance of a left wing government destroying itself. Later instances have multiplied, that of Chile being the latest but not the last. The process, moreover, is always much the same. The lesson, which socialists never learn, is that a government's position must be unstable if it rests on the active hostility of people who have been cheated out of their savings. An embittered middle class does not readily assemble, demonstrate and riot. It offers, instead, a background for military revolt. In this connection we must remember that the modern army has a middle class origin. All the technical branches recruit men of more than average education. All the non-commissioned officers have middle-class ambitions. These are not men who have been recruited from the dregs of the population. The result is that the middle class resentments are readily reflected in the armed forces. It is there that a middle class revolt is likely to begin.

It would be natural to ask at this stage why ministers of presumably average intelligence will fail to foresee the results of their own policy. Every school child must know that overspending is the cause of inflation. Does no minister point this out to his less educated colleagues? Is there no economist at hand to advise them? In point of fact, the voice of wisdom does occasionally make itself heard. There are ministers who will talk of financial caution and the need for a balanced budget. Nor are they without influence for they sometimes gain a measure of agreement. There is talk of economy but it takes only one direction. This is the government's fourth step towards self-destruction. There must be a cut in the estimates for the armed forces! There must be a reduction in the number of ships and aircraft. More to the point, infantry units must be disbanded, and all the more distant outposts must be evacuated.

Why are the first economies to affect the Ministry of Defence? Plainly because these cuts in expenditure will lose the minimum of votes. There is, however, another motive, for the armed forces are probably conservative, and their reduction in strength will weaken the anti-socialist opposition. Generals and colonels are political opponents, and the effect of their early and compulsory retirement will be to leave them impotent and penniless. What the ministers fail to observe is that the abandonment of distant fortresses gives an added importance to the home-based troops. They equally fail to appreciate that the disbanding of units B and C gives an added importance to unit A. Without the least idea of what they are doing, ministers have created a Praetorian Guard, the divisions of which are quartered near the capital city. In selecting the officers for compulsory retirement, the minister for war will naturally have chosen to eliminate all whose loyalty is doubtful. It is a question, however, whether those who remain are any more reliable. They are men, after all, who may expect to be removed at any time as redundant. Given a fluid political situation, they might well be found to have ideas of their own.

The fifth step towards self-destruction is not perhaps the easiest to understand. One would expect that a government which had drastically reduced its armed forces would pursue an external policy of caution. That is not, however, what history has to teach. For governments of the left are shrill in their ideology and loud in their condemnation of other countries which deviate from the true faith. The British who voted for unilateral disarmament in the years between World Wars I and II were eager to make enemies of Italy, Germany and Russia. Their descendants have been as keen to denounce as they have been reluctant to serve. The real and immediate danger lies, however, in forming a foreign policy which is not, in fact, in the country's best interests. The intention may be to further the cause of socialism in the world. The intention may be to divert attention from domestic difficulties and unrest. The intention may be altruistic, idealistic and wholly admirable, but the results are usually disappointing. We have, to begin with, the subsidies paid to what are hopefully described as developing nations: money which the donors do not possess paid out to recipients who might otherwise embrace communism. Then we have the diplomatic or military defeat which is the result of an inability to decide what exactly we are trying to do. We have finally the despatch of troops sent to intervene between warring tribes and religious groups. Such by now is the shortage of infantry that men who are to be misused as policemen are drawn from the artillery or from the engineers. The usual result is to antagonise both sides in the conflict and leave your men to be pelted with stones from two directions and forbidden, of course, to open fire. Here is an infallible method of creating discontent among one's own forces. After a few years of this official blundering they will be fit for treasons, stratagems and spoils.

Come now to the last step of all, the one which leads to actual destruction. A massive bureaucracy has been placed between the government and the people. The system of administration has been centralised to the point of lunacy. A failure to balance the accounts has inaugurated a period of roaring inflation, ruining the middle class in the process. Economies have been made but solely at the expense of the armed forces. The country's impotence has been exposed by its tame reaction to both insult and injury. What troops remain have been misused in some ideological cause. The bonfire has been built up in five easy stages and it only remains to set it alight. How is this done? To follow the sixth and last step one must realise, first of all, that the ministers who control a well-meaning, liberal, socialist, mildly corrupt and democratically elected government are people with the loftiest ideals. They are not merely wise and confronted by opponents who are mistaken. They are also normally good and confronted by opponents who are evil. It is always a question whether their own finances would bear investigation, but that is, after all, a minor matter. In all matters of importance they are conscious of their own public integrity. They are working for peace, for the welfare of their constituents and for the good of mankind.

It is this conscious rectitude which drives them, sooner of later, into violence. They are democrats, of course, and they believe in the upholding of law and order. But when there is opposition to what they know to be right, when there is the possibility that they may be out-voted, they are driven to conclude that innocent people have been deliberately and wickedly deceived. For a strictly limited period the whole democratic process must be suspended. This is a hard decision but one readily reached by people whose motives are, after all, above suspicion. No one could suppose for a moment that they want power for its own sake. It is clear, however, that their more vocal opponents must be arrested. Heaven knows how reluctant they are to take this step. It goes against all that they have believed and taught. They know that they will be accused of inconsistency, but this is part of the burden they have to bear. The arrests are made and the idealists have now placed themselves on a level with the seediest crooks who have ever opposed them. The moment has come for the *coup d'etat*.

In its simplest form the *coup d'etat* begins when a disgruntled lieutenant-colonel holds a secret meeting with two other disgruntled officers of the same rank, all due for retirement next year. Their respective battalions are all quartered in the Southroad Barracks, just outside the capital city. Why is it normally a lieutenant-colonel who plans the *coup*? Because the lieutenant-colonel is the most senior officer who actually has any troops of his own — a brigadier has only a headquarters. Having co-opted a major who commands a squadron of tanks (essential in order to be televised), the three lieutenant-colonels reach an agreement; A is to be president, B is to be commander-in-chief, C is to be head of the national bank and D (the major) is to be chief of police. They have between them what amounts to a Brigade Group, and this is quite sufficient to occupy the Palace, the government offices, the broadcasting station, the telephone exchange, the central police station and the airport. Some capital cities are somewhat dispersed and could not be occupied by less than a division. In general, however, government policy has been to concentrate all the levers of power in the smallest area, making the whole target highly vulnerable. There is no provincial capital with a life of its own. There are no leaders other than the handful arrested during the first half-hour of the rising. The arrests made — the work of a platoon — it remains to make the vital television announcement.

In this the public will be told that the government has fallen, that no other government could be formed in the ordinary way, and that Colonel A has consented to accept the post of prime minister on a purely temporary basis. In doing this he yielded reluctantly to the entreaties of politicians drawn from all parties. Nor would he have agreed to this had he not been promised the help of Colonels B and C, together with that of Major D. He cannot speak too highly of the patriotism and self-sacrifice these officers have shown by coming forward at this time. Colonel A wishes it to be known that the situation is quite normal and that there has been no disturbance of any kind. Purely as a precautionary measure, some troops, including tanks, have been moved into the centre of the capital, from which the public has been temporarily excluded. All is quiet, however, and the road-blocks will have gone by morning. There is no cause for alarm, and there should be business as usual as from midday tomorrow, the hour at which the stock exchange will reopen. On this note the announcement ends.

There is statistical proof that the majority of *coups d'etat* succeed, and there can be no doubt that most of them have been carefully planned with previous infiltration of the secret service, of the police force and of the government departments. According to Edward Lutt-wak, "A *coup* consists of the infiltration of a small but critical segment of the state apparatus, which is then used to displace the government from its control of the remainder" (*idem*, p. 27). The object of the exercise is to use the power of the State against itself. This must usually involve careful preparation. The fact remains, however, that the undermining of the government will previously have been done by the government itself. It is the practice of democratic politicians to saw off the tree branch on which they are sitting. The task for the actual conspirators is thus simplified. Where they need most skill is in handling personalities, seeing to details and synchronising the action. The task is complex and highly dangerous, for the government initially holds all the cards, but political stability is not a feature of the ages:

> *If those who carry out the coup appear to shatter such a powerful structure merely by seizing a few buildings, arresting some political figures and 'liberating' the radio station, it is because their crucial achievement passes unnoticed. This is the dangerous and elaborate process by which the armed forces and the other means of coercion are neutralised, and the political forces temporarily forced into passivity.*

Luttwak, pp. 57-58

This is true but not perhaps the whole truth. There are instances when the government has virtually committed suicide.

If the *coup d'état* succeeds, Colonel A becomes dictator and rules through the bureaucracy which his democratic predecessors have created. But the *coup d'état* may fail and we have seen that it frequently does. This is often the result of the conspirators failing to neutralise some part of the armed forces. Colonel A can rely on his brigade (the 97th) but he has failed to notice that Colonel X, working closely with Colonels Y and Z, has secured control of another brigade (the 94th), elements of which moved yesterday into the Northroad Barracks. When Colonel A sets up his headquarters in the Palace, he learns to his dismay that the broadcasting station and airport have been occupied by troops of the 94th Brigade. On the radio he hears the voice of Colonel X informing the public that certain army units have mutinied, but that there is no cause for alarm. "Loyal" army units, in vastly superior numbers, are moving into the city centre and will have everything under control by nightfall. There is a half-hearted skirmish, with the occasional stutter of machine-gun fire, and then the noise of fighting dies away. Next morning Colonel X announces on television that members of the cabinet have asked him to assume office as prime minister, following the tragic death of his predecessor (shot by the rebels). All is now quiet in the capital and certain army officers will be tried very shortly by a military court. Two cabinet ministers have resigned and have been replaced by Colonels Y and Z, of whose patriotism and self-sacrifice he cannot speak too highly. There is no cause for alarm and there should be business as usual as from mid-day tomorrow, the hour at which the stock exchange will re-open.

The success of a *coup d'état,* or its suppression, should equally end in dictatorship, but this story is not invariable. There have been instances of a feeble government collapsing on its own, financially and intellectually bankrupt. There have been examples of the mob sacking the administration centre. Once a government has taken the six steps to destruction, the result can be chaos in different forms. But chaos is unwanted except by a very few. There is a prompt reaction and order has to be restored by someone. By the time the firing has died away a dictator will have assumed office. Forced initially to act with vigor, putting the mob leaders before a firing squad, the dictator finds that he cannot resign without sharing their fate. So he must normally remain in power for as long as he lives. There is no reason to assume that dictatorship is of necessity a bad form of government, and there are certainly times when no other form of government is even possible. But a dictator's rule is marred by a certain instability. It depends on the life of one man who cannot live forever and may not live for long. To maintain his dictatorial power, that one ruler must surround himself with mediocre lieutenants, no one able enough to be a danger and no one designated as successor. So the death of the dictator is apt to produce chaos again. From the point of view of stability it would be best if the dictatorship could turn into monarchy — as in ancient times it frequently did — but there are more instances in modern times of more confusion ending in another dictatorship. For all this chaos the people ultimately responsible were the well-meaning liberal socialists who wrecked democracy and who incidently destroyed themselves.

No object would be served by any lengthy discussion of dictatorship as a form of rule. It has certain merits, but it is generally regarded as a temporary expedient. It is true that dictators may remain in power for many years but the effect of this is usually unfortunate. In the first place, the dictator must age with time, losing his capacity for making decisions, losing his popular influence and losing, finally, his sense of reality. And the longer he rules the greater the reaction will be to his form of rule. If the establishment of the dictatorship was essential when it began and useful over the next decade, its final results are apt to be very destructive indeed. So we can fairly ask whether anything could be done to prevent today's folly leading to tomorrow's misery. Could we avert the coming catastrophe if we had more energy and lived, while still effective, to a greater age? In attempting to answer this question we must remember that the decline of an individual's effectiveness is related to his life expectation, the same being true of each civilisation as a whole. We have seen that over-centralisation and socialism, bureaucracy and inflation lead to the errors in policy which precede collapse. Could this process have been checked by an improvement in man's *individual* performance? There are reasons for thinking that this is possible, although there may be no certainty as yet that it can be done.

Could we profit more from the wisdom of age? The complaint of youth is that the old are cumbered with obsolete ideas, that they do not understand the world of today. Those who served under Winston Churchill in World War II had thus the unworthy suspicion at times that he was still fighting the Battle of Omdurman of 1898. There may often be an element of truth in this complaint, but the more serious criticism of the old is that they may be content with arrangements which will last their time. Human motives are hard to analyse, but it is a fact that we have only a limited interest in events which will take place after we are dead.

Power tends to be vested in men aged fifty to sixty-five. They plan for up to ten or fifteen years ahead, but with interest lessening as time goes on. There was a time when people were ready to protect their children's interests, but this foresight involved the purchase of estates and the planting of avenues, the entail of property and alliances by marriage. These plans relate to a former age. We can no longer attempt to leave a fortune, and it would probably be worthless, anyway, before our heir could inherit. We can no longer plan anything for our children, nor can we readily imagine what sort of life they are to lead. That being so, we are still less able to plan on behalf of other people or, indeed, for the whole community. We are too little concerned with the long-term results of the policies we are asked to approve, and this is especially apparent in matters of finance. We are ready to let some future generation pay for our mistakes. By the day of reckoning we shall no longer be in power and the likelihood is that we shall no longer be alive. Our currency will be worthless, but why should we worry about that now?

The position and our attitude would be different if we were to live for a century. We should then have to live with the results of our improvidence. The reckless expenditure of today would not fall entirely on our grandchildren but would curtail the amount of our own pension. We should still be there when the bill came to be presented, and we might have some awkward questions to answer. Given a longer active life we should certainly have to retire before we were worn out. We could not keep our successors out of office indefinitely. But we should certainly change our whole attitude towards the future, knowing that we ourselves would be involved in it. We should, for one thing, accept the fact that the sequence of events we have just described, from over-centralisation to the inevitable *coup d'etat*, must all happen within our own lifetime. We must ourselves live under the dictatorship we have brought about. Faced with this prospect, we might well think again, asking whether our bureaucracy is really needed.

A more responsible attitude towards the future, is not, however, the only advantage we should derive from a longer life. For there would be the additional advantage of our remaining active for a longer period and being able to offer some useful advice for perhaps as long again. And one thing we should have learnt over the longer lifetime is the importance of inherited talent. Our present age is one in which children are deemed to be more or less equal at birth, their subsequent progress or lack of it being attributed to differences in upbringing and education. This old conviction is not, at first glance, easy to explain. It would seem, however, that the idea is current among people who have been brought up in rootless suburbs and who have never seen the grandparents of their neighbours and friends, nor for that matter their grandchildren. Those who live to the age of a hundred, perceptive to the end, would know their own great-grandchildren, as also their own great-grandparents, and would realise, as country folk have always known, that there are strong family characteristics, members of one clan being avaricious and members of another being mostly daft. They would give some thought to the problems of breeding and care less, perhaps, about what people learn or fail to learn at school.

A final advantage which might result from a prolonged life span would be the elimination of the inertia which now precedes retirement. There are men of sixty-four who are perfectly capable of transacting all the business which comes to them. The decisions are made, the meetings held, the telegrams are drafted, the letters signed. All this activity falls within the boundaries of the existing routine. What the elderly ministers lack is the energy to go on after the day's business has been transacted. A man with dynamic energy would go beyond the boundaries of the existing routine and ask whether the business is being dealt with in the best possible way. Going further, he might query whether some of the business need come to him at all. He might decide, for that matter, that the expenditure should be reduced by ten percent this year and again by the same percentage in the following year. It requires little energy to carry on as usual, following precedent and avoiding friction. It requires tremendous energy to go beyond that and ask why it takes so many people to produce such a poor result. With only one or two years to go most of us are ready to accept things as they are. But what if there were many years ahead of us and further years to be spent in an active retirement? Instead of saying, "I shall leave that to my successor," we might set about doing what needs to be done.

For many people the top executive position is the reward for long and faithful service. After years of loyal subordination, number two succeeds at last to the chief post, which carries with it all sorts of honour and prestige. He looks back over all the blunders he has avoided, over all the disagreements he has managed to divert, over all the decisions he has contrived to postpone. He has done well and he deserves this last and all-important promotion. He receives the sincere congratulations of men who frankly recognise his superior ability. Being within five years of retirement, he has one year to learn the business from this new angle. During the last two years he will be grooming his successor and deciding against any plan he cannot complete.

Two years remain in which to make his own contribution, changing what needs to be changed. But are two years enough? Two years are probably ample (in war-time it would be done in two weeks) but it is easy to think otherwise. It would take time to explain and prepare, time to reorganise and allocate, time to overcome all the possible objections. And what if it were a failure, with the decisions subsequently reversed? Taking all these points into consideration it is reasonable to conclude that time is insufficient, and that it is better to leave things as they are. These are the causes of inertia, and they would be swept away by an injection of energy which would allow number one to remain in office for another five years or even ten. If the means exist for injecting fresh energy into our affairs, we should do well to study them. It is the purpose of this book to show that such an injection is not impossible, that such a miracle may yet occur.

CHAPTER 6

The Death Wish

It was commonly assumed during the last century and especially towards its close that society was making progress towards a bright future. It was easy to point, on the one hand, to the London slums as described by Dickens, and on the other hand, to the garden suburbs being planned for their employees by Lever Brothers and Rowntree's. The new tenements were arguably superior to the old hovels. The council houses were sometimes of pleasant design, well sited and soon to be well furnished. There were manifest improvements in cleanliness, clothing, education and food. The middle class had secured many advantages previously restricted to the upper class. The lower classes now gained some privileges hitherto confined to the middle class. One could talk of progress without irony and indeed with some confidence. In 1900 it was a reality and the appearance of it lingered perhaps until 1950, unassisted by two world wars but affording encouragement to the optimist. Confidence in the future is represented, above all, by the publication of utopian literature. *Utopia* itself appeared in 1516; there were a number of eighteenth and nineteenth century imitations leading up to William Morris's *News from Nowhere* in 1890.

About the last example of this type of book was H. G. Well's *Modern Utopia* of 1905, to be followed in sharp contrast by *Brave New World*, published by Aldous Huxley in 1932, and the still more pessimistic *Nineteen Eighty-Four* by George Orwell (1949). Progress as an idea has been more or less confined to politicians since about the middle of the century.

In theory the end of progress could usher in a period of stagnation or stability but that is not what has happened. What is not growing is usually dying, and ours is a society of which the end is not very remote. We have watched the process of over-centralisation, over-taxation and socialism. We have watched an upper class become penniless, endowed as it is with a gift for survival. We are watching a middle class face ruin through inflation. The lower classes remain prosperous in the short term, but they are turning into a characterless mass. The civilisation of Western Europe has derived its quality from its emphasis on the individual. It has thus contrasted with an Oriental world in which the emphasis has been on the tribe, the clan or the mob. With a population far too big for our land area, with far too high a birthrate, we are witnesses to the process by which individuality is lost in the swelling crowd. We have seen that the first result of over-population is soil erosion, the impoverishment of the fields and the lengthening of the distance between the people and the soil. We now see the second revolt, due to the pressure of people upon each other. Overcrowding is accomplished by various forms of competition and friction, the loss of individuality being an irritant in itself. It is true that these stresses and strains lead to the loss of fertility but not until the damage has been done. There are already too many people in existence, and the declining birthrate offers no immediate remedy. A city like New York (let alone Calcutta) offers the picture of a population which is too big to handle. The whole situation is plainly out of control.

In an industrialised society the workpeople have little or no interest in their mechanical work. They live for the tea-break, for the end of the shift, the end of the day's work, for the weekend, for the annual holidays. In so far as they have any views about their working life, they are mainly expressed through trade unions which exist to obtain higher pay for shorter hours of work. Trade unions might have had a colourful and romantic history, but their story has been uninspiring and dull. They have always been open to criticism on three grounds. They are unconstructive, they are aggressive and they exemplify the failings of any other great organisation. As remarked by one of the authors in a previous work:

As compared with a medieval craft guild, the trade union has shown no interest in its particular trade. Members do not ask each other how their product can be improved, how their own firm can secure a lead over others, or how the industry as a whole can better serve the public and the world. While a craft guild was concerned with qualifications for membership, schemes of training, tests of competence and penalties for fraud, the unions have merely been intent on preventing the employment of non-members. Their interest has not been in the business or the product but in the wage levels applied to their or any comparable trade. Loyalty has often been intense but kept to the horizontal plane, a loyalty to workmates at the narrowed, to the working class at widest, but seldom to the work as such.

C. Northcote Parkinson
Left Luggage, London, 1967, p. 70

It is not quite true to say that satisfaction and pride in workmanship have vanished. They have dwindled, however, and there are large numbers of people who would seem to have none at all. For them an important interest in life has been lost at the outset. They merely ask as much as they dare for doing as little as they can.

It is the task of the management staff to inspire the men and women on the factory floor, but labour relations are apt to be very bad indeed. At the top there can be frequent mergers and changes in ownership. A point may be reached when the employees have no idea who the directors are. Things become worse still when management becomes scientific. By donning the scientist's white coat and taking refuge in the firm's laboratory, the newest type of managing directors become intellectually remote from their work force. The computer stands between the manager and the managed, and the human relationships are worse than ever. The personnel manager comes to the rescue but with an applied psychology which still further weakens any actual contact. There is probably a lack of energy on either side, and the final result is to have a work force mainly intent on watching the clock and marking the calendar. But to write off all working hours as nothingness, a routine to survive, a horror to endure, is to give a new importance to the hours of leisure. If nothing of interest takes place from (say) nine to five, except when there is a strike, it matters all the more what happens between five and nine. Shorter working hours may merely mean overtime pay, but what when the hours worked are actually shorter and the hours of leisure correspondingly prolonged? How are the leisure hours actually spent? In what directions are the pent-up engines released? What do people do with their time?

The Victorian middle class had scanty hours of leisure, as we know. The tradition had been to work through all the hours of daylight, but the invention of gaslight made it possible to work round the clock, which some of them tried to do. Hours were eventually stabilised, but they remained very long, the tempo broken only by Sundays and certain established holidays. One is impressed, however, by the variety of hobbies which people would pursue. People played the piano, sang, recited and acted charades. They operated puppet theatres and magic lanterns, built elaborate models, collected stamps and developed their own photographs. There were choral societies, magic circles for the improvement of conjuring tricks, groups which studied natural history and a host of queer religions. The Christmas period was the occasion for a score of now forgotten parlour games, with molten lead dropped into cold water, walnut shells with lit tapers circling a miniature sea and games in which blindfold players had to pin the tail on the donkey. Victorian clothes might be hideous and dull but Victorian imagination would seem to have been very much alive. Summer activities were widened with the coming of the bicycle, there being new opportunities for sketching, geology and the identification of wild flowers. It might have seemed probable that the lower classes, given more leisure, would copy the middle class lead in developing their leisure activities. By then, however, times had changed and technology had influenced all classes alike, mechanising their leisure as well as their work.

Dwellers in the modern industrial city and its suburbs are all more or less trapped in a machine-made and standardised way of life. They have some advantages which their great-grandparents may have lacked: running water, light, heat and public transport. But they are filled with a longing to escape from the dreary surroundings that are their prisons. The car offers them the means of escape at the weekend, but they have found that drugs may offer them an easier method. Oldest of the drugs available is alcohol, and this has always provided the quickest way out of Huddersfield or Rochdale. Seated among a group of companions and provided with sufficient drink for the purpose, a man or woman can move to another world where people are friendly and witty, cheerful and easily amused. He can forget all reality in a fog of tobacco smoke and the sound of a rousing chorus. Tobacco or nicotine is a mild narcotic, and a cause of lung cancer, but it plays a part in allowing people to escape from the world in which they live. Gambling is another drug, the gambler being able to daydream about the wealth he may gain, with luck, and the life of luxury which will result. No actual harm results until the gambler bets more than he can afford to lose. There are elderly people who know only these three drugs and find them sufficient as a means of escape. Among younger folk and among many now middle-aged there is a wider knowledge of other drugs. Without rejecting alcohol and tobacco they turn to other and more drastic means of avoiding reality. Perhaps the first of these more powerful drugs is speed: the noise and onset of the racing car or the motor-cycle.

That speed is a drug has long been known, but the idea of it is confused with certain other psychological implications. Ignoring these for the moment, we should note that people value the impression of speed rather than speed itself. Jet aircraft approach the speed of sound without giving passengers a feeling of undue haste. The more powerful type of motorcycle, on the other hand, roars out a message of doom. In helmet and goggles, in leather jacket and brightly coloured scarf, the rider feels like the terror of the highways, the wind pressure mounting and the landscape seen as a mere blur. Given a female companion on the pillion, the sensations are more complex. Our present concern, however, is with speed and noise, and there can be no doubt that the sound of the engine is essential to the thrill. As essential, perhaps, is the element of risk. As compared with the motorist, the rider of a motorcycle is without protection. If he crashes at seventy miles an hour he will probably break his neck. It is an awareness of this that gives an additional swagger to his gait. But his enjoyment centres, nevertheless, on the mere sensation of speed. When rather older he may graduate to the sports car or even to the racing track. With the sports car, something of convenience and comfort has been sacrificed to the appearance rather than the reality of speed. The vehicle takes its driver away from the dull streets of Middlesborough or Bolton, but not into a pleasanter landscape so much as into a world of fantasy. Some boastful chatter is involved and a great deal of fiddling with engines, but there can be no doubt that speed is essentially a drug.

Next to speed comes noise. A generation which is strangely unmusical has grown up in a world of amplified sound. Basis of the noise is the African drum-beat, the rhythm of the black dance, the bellowings of the untrained voice. It is more than probable that these noises do permanent damage to the ear-drums and the brain. Be that, however, as it may, the effect of the drum-beat is hypnotic. The addict goes into a sort of trance, unaware of anything else, inaccessible to any other message. The strident noise is a sort of anaesthetic, and those who listen and respond have the faraway stare of a drug addict. Their urge was to escape from their surroundings and this they have done, more effortlessly and perhaps more cheaply than it could have been done on a motorcycle. All they bought was a stereo record player and the latest popular long-playing record. No knowledge is required, no skill of any kind. All they need is a noise-filled room with each other for company. In so far as any words are audible they would seem to have a sexual implication, but one may doubt whether the sex aspects are important. What would seem to matter is the hypnosis, sought even by those who have not reached puberty. Beyond the mere impact of noise is the added element, on occasion, of mass hysteria. As among the primitive people who first discovered the rhythm, the presence of a crowd adds to the effect. This is one more way, in fact, in which we have moved from the concept of the individual to the cult of the mob. As voodoo worshippers proved long ago, mere noise and numbers can be a very powerful drug indeed.

Violence is yet another drug and it comes in two different forms, the theoretical and the practical. There is nothing new about this, acts of violence being lovingly described in our most ancient works of literature. What is new is the mechanised entertainment which allows us to witness violence every day. There is a difference, at least in theory, between the real and the dramatised forms of violence. To watch a riot or public execution on a televised news programme is not quite the same thing as to watch a simulated battle between cowboys and Indians. But is the effect so different? The one thing certain is that we have come to accept violence as a normal thing in our lives. By following the dramatic event, the news camera has given us a false picture of the world with bombs bursting in Belfast every minute. There have been murders watched by millions of viewers, and riots which have been staged for the camera's benefit.

And just as Spanish children are acclimatised to bloodshed in the bull-ring, an arena dating back to Roman times, we now have a similar indoctrination on television and in the cinema, staged in colour with all the appropriate sound effects. In general, the people most interested in bloodshed are those without experience of war. For a younger generation, remote from the battlefield or blitz, there would seem to be a fatal fascination in mere violence. Film directors are usually quite ignorant of firearms, a circumstance which detracts from the realism of their battle scenes, but corpses nevertheless litter the "western" film set with almost Shakespearian profusion. As each film outdoes the last, we end with the X film of today, the horror show which young people are not supposed to see. In apparently respectable cinemas there will be nothing but X films for weeks at a time, the managers explaining that these are demanded by patrons aged between eighteen and twenty-six, an age-group comprising much of the modern audience. This demand for the horror film, with vampires, werewolves and added touches of black magic, is something not easy to explain. It would seem to suggest, however, that life for many people is deadly dull and that an hour of Frankenstein or Dracula takes the mind off life as it has to be lived. To that extent the gruesome nature of the film is witness to the dullness of actual existence. Only a terribly stale sandwich could need as much mustard as that.

Whether hooliganism in the streets is a result of violence on television is a matter for argument. Whatever the evidence may suggest, however, we know that both are on the increase and that each can be regarded as a drug. While it is true that mugging or robbery is a form of theft, there is also many an assault which seems to be pointless, an act of violence for its own sake. As much can be said about damage to property, the wrecking of telephone kiosks and the defacing of posters. There is much damage for the sake of damage, and this again reflects on the boredom from which many young people suffer and especially all those who are kept too long at school. Many are more or less imbecile, but it is boredom which makes

them react in that particular way. Nor is
violence always a product of the slums. Even
children in the more prosperous suburbs will
feel that life is pointless and that a little shop-
lifting may serve to add excitement. In all these
instances the motive is to escape from the
dullness of existence and run the risk of a possible arrest and trial. The pleasure is not in
spending the night in the cells but in the feeling
that arrest is possible, that the risk is being
run. This is another form of drug and one which
is all too easily procured.

A last form of drug (narcotics apart) is
that of sex. It is inevitable and natural that people should have an interest in sex and it need
cause no surprise that some people have sexual
tastes which other people disapprove. We have
no occasion here to discuss these preferences or
attempt to decide what harm, if any, they involve. Where sex becomes a drug is not where it
deviates from an accepted pattern but where it
supersedes all other form of activity. We are all
familiar with the novel or play in which we are
invited to worry about whether A is to sleep
with B or C. All three characters being quite
without interest, we don't care what A decides
to do. What is more to the point, however, is
that the plot is insufficient. To give the story
any substance A must have a career as well as a
love-life, B must have committed a crime and C
must be a communist agent. It should be made

apparent, in fact, that sex, while important, is not the whole life. Sex becomes a drug when it excludes everything else, and there are works on the bookstall which do exactly that, their circulation seeming to prove that some people have no other interest. But books with even a strong sex angle (the *Iliad* being one of them) are more successful if they also touch upon politics and strategy, poetry and humour. Where books and motion pictures in which sex is the only theme multiply, we are forced to conclude that sex has become for many people an obsession or drug. It offers, in fact, another escape from reality.

In addition to the drugs already described there are the actual narcotics. To discuss these at length would involve writing another book, but to ignore them would be absurd. Drugs, we learn, are either mild or potent and some people draw a sharp distinction between drugs thought to be relatively harmless and drugs known to be dangerous or lethal. There are no grounds for making this distinction, and one research psychiatrist considers that marijuana is the most dangerous drug we have to contend with:

Its early use is beguiling. It gives the illusion of feeling good. The user is not aware of the beginning loss of mental functioning. I have never seen an exception to the obser-

vation that marijuana impairs the user's ability to judge the loss of his own mental functioning.

Dr. Harvey Powell

The present epidemic of drug taking in the Western world seems to date from 1965 and specifically from the "Revolution" which took place that year on the Berkeley Campus of the University of California. Like student unrest itself, it spread from there to other American universities, to colleges and high schools, to the public at large and to the armed forces. It played a significant part in undermining the morale of the American troops in Vietnam. It has now penetrated Western society as a whole, its progress greatly hastened by a lack of information about its short-term and long-term effects. Knowing little about it and assured by addicts that their insight had been improved by the drug, a number of physicians stated publicly that they had no proof of the drug being harmful and that its use should be legalised and controlled. That they had no proof, at that stage, was perfectly true. Evidence concerning the damage done began to accumulate over the following years and was finally summarised in evidence given before a Congressional subcommittee in May, 1974. It became perfectly clear that the marijuana addict soon begins to lose memory and time sense, going on (with heavier doses) to lose all capacity for logical thought and ending in a world of paranoid illusion. From Professor Hardin B. Jones came the following evidence:

> *I have personally interviewed more than 16,000 drug users, most of whom use cannabis... The awful fact is that we are caught up in the most destructive epidemic of cannabis abuse the world has yet known. But the magnitude of the disaster has not been recognised and corrective remedies have not been applied...*
>
> *Even though of the average Freshmen coming to the University, only about 1 in 6 or 1 in 8 use cannabis when they come in, each successive year they stay the fraction that uses cannabis or other drugs increases, so by the time they graduate, considerably better than 90 percent are experienced cannabis users... The problem is not going away...*
>
> *As an expert in human addiction effects, I point out that the chromosome damage found by Professor Stenchever, even in those who use cannabis moderately, is roughly the same type and degree of damage as in persons surviving atomic bombing with a heavy level of radiation exposure — approximately 150 roentgens.*
>
> *Dr. Heath has presented direct observation in humans that use of cannabis*

*results in persistent poisoning of the deep
centers of the brain necessary for the
awareness of pleasure . . . Dr. Heath has, in
a sense, shown by direct measurement that
cannabis poisons the very part of the brain
that allows full awareness of being alive.*

*There is perhaps no greater hell, even
with pain, than not to be able to feel alive.
Those who are not able to feel alive will
even seek pain to get relief from this
remorse. And that is the hell that is pro-
jected for those who use cannabis.*

*Monthly Publication by the Thomas
Jefferson Research Center*
Number 107
February, 1975

It is widely supposed that cannabis, used
in moderation is safe in itself but may lead the
addict into use of the stronger and more
dangerous drugs like heroin. There could be no
greater mistake. Cannabis is highly dangerous
and no worse drug is needed to bring about
pathological patterns of thought. Perhaps the
worst result of its use is that the addict has a
strong urge to convert others to its use. This
urge is a symptom of cannabis addiction, a
result of the brain's damage which the addict
has sustained and a principal cause of the
habit's spreading.

Cannabis does immense damage, but there are worse drugs, and the user of marijuana may well graduate to these. Habit-forming drugs, apart from alcohol and nicotine, are mostly based upon either opium or cocaine. Morphine addiction makes the patient self-centred, unreliable, immoral and depraved. General health suffers as well as intelligence, the symptoms including insomnia, anaemia, loss of weight and indigestion. Cure is unlikely with the treatment succeeding in no more than ten percent of the patients treated. Cocaine produces, initially, a feeling of well-being and stimulation which is followed, however, by physical and mental degradation, hallucinations and suicidal impulses, the general condition being almost incurable. Heroin is one drug in common use, a sedative akin to morphine. There are other drugs, derivatives of opium, used throughout the Oriental world and now penetrating the West. The danger of traffic in opium led the United Nations to set up a narcotics commission in 1946. More has thus come to be known about the trade in drugs, but there has been no very dramatic success in ending it. Consignments seized by the police are presumably a small fraction of the consignments which are duly delivered. Some criminals are punished but the trade goes on as before.

The drugs available are nicotine, alcohol, gambling, speed, noise, violence, sex, cannabis, opium and cocaine. It is not to our purpose to discuss whether any of these are harmless or whether the more harmful habits can be cured. The point on which we must insist is that the use of a drug represents, first and foremost, an attempt to escape from reality. The significant fact is that the addict has rejected the environment in which he finds himself. He has little or no interest in his work, his home, his relatives or children, his leisure activities or amusements. He wants to escape into a world of illusion. He wants essentially to die. All or most of the drugs listed can bring death nearer, and some can be fatal almost at once. Behind the drug addiction lies, therefore, the death wish, a desire to end it all, perhaps for a time and more likely for good. For people with satisfying work to do, and with spare-time occupations which are sufficiently absorbing, the day is not long enough and life itself is too short. "Pastimes" have been devised to pass the time and may serve that purpose well, but they have no appeal to the creative worker who can scarcely find time for all he wants to do. But when we turn from pastimes, harmless in themselves, and seek oblivion in drugs, we reveal the failure of our lives. That the drugs may be lethal is almost beside the point. The essential fact is that the drug-taker has lost interest in life. All he has to keep him alive is the irresolution which alone prevents him from pressing the trigger or turning on the gas.

This is the death wish as it affects the individual. But it also influences the institution and the State. How often do we see an ailing industry, its life somehow prolonged into a century to which it has no obvious relevance, companies formed to manufacture things long obsolete, factories producing goods which must have been fashionable at the beginning of the century. Looking at these quaint survivals, surprised to find that they are still in existence, we might reasonably conclude that they would be safe at least from industrial dispute. We picture the directors as men afraid even to sneeze in case it should overturn the tottering and rusting machinery. We picture the workers tiptoeing round the factory floor for fear that a careless stumble might bring the roof down, upheld as it is by cobwebs. We picture the elderly members of the public who buy the firm's product from force of habit but who would switch to another brand if the supply were to fail for as much as an instant. In such a dead-and-alive company we might assume that a strike would be impossible. But these are exactly the circumstances in which men will agree to down tools. The more precarious the situation the more certain it is that a strike will take place, leading to a loss of business, a financial crisis and a final liquidation. The factory is closed, the site has been sold and the men are unemployed. How could the employees be so foolish? Did they not realise what the result of their action would be? They knew well enough, but they had the death wish. One way to stop worrying about the future is to bring about the feared disaster. Subconsciously, at least, the men wanted their factory to close.

Nor are governments very different. With them as shown earlier, the steps towards self-destruction are all sufficiently well-known. An ordinary dull democracy allows its bureaucracy to multiply and entrench itself. It centralises its administration in a central area of its capital city. Embracing the socialist creed, it centralises its industry and commerce in the same way, ruining a great number of people whose opposition becomes implacable. The process of vote-buying starts a process of inflation, which ruins the middle-class from which the armed forces are officered. A belated demand for economy leads to a disbandment of a part of the armed forces, giving added importance to the part which remains. Those remaining forces are then misused in pursuit of some ideological stupidity. At the next crisis the government announces that there is a national emergency and that all its political opponents have been arrested. Then comes the *coup d'etat*. Its inevitability is perfectly obvious, and we wonder how the ministers can have failed to foresee their own fate. But were they really as stupid as that? Or is this another instance of the subconscious death wish? Were they really wanting to end the farce? This is not an easy question to answer, but instances of self-destruction according to this sort of formula are very numerous and go far back in history. When we consider many of the current leaders of the West, we can fairly ask whether they even want to survive. Perhaps the death wish has doomed their civilisation as a whole.

When we study the death wish which propels the individual, the institution or the community towards destruction, we do well to direct our attention towards the earlier situation from which its later troubles were to stem. The story does not begin with students at Berkeley who took to cannabis and staged a revolt. It begins with a university which had grown too big and complex, too burdened with its procedures, with too few teachers of distinction and too many students who were unsuitable for admission. The students had, many of them, come to the university in search of inspiration, excitement, leadership and authority. The university had none of these things, however, to offer. Its high officers and teachers were remote, its classes were too large, its lectures were dull and its students were bored. In the same way the strike in the factory had its origin in a general situation which was hopeless, with obsolete machinery turning out a shoddy stream of outdated goods. Nor was the dull republic any better when it took those first steps towards self-destruction. It died of socialism but what better alternatives had its conservatives to offer? Had they been full of vitality and adventure, imaginative in their leadership, poetic in their speech? Or had they been as dreary as their opponents and as empty of ideas? Was not the republic stifled by mediocrity before it came to be strangled by the do-gooders? The causes of decay are often further back in history then we are apt to assume. The rise of Adolf Hitler was possible only because of the failure of his predecessors in power. Whatever he did to cause sedition, he did it against a familiar background: that picture of an awful complacency.

This brings us back again to the need for energy. We have politicians and civil servants who can transact the day's business. We have a legislature able to deal with at least half of its intended programme for the year. But the real task begins at the point where our leaders finish. When all the current questions have been settled, it is not the moment to go home, and still less so when much of the business remains to finish. It is the moment, rather, when we should turn to something more important: the matters we initiate rather than the prob-

lems thrown at us. What are we trying to do
and how shall we set about it? How do we make
it colourful and interesting? To what does our
present policy lead? Can we simplify the procedure? Can we employ a smaller number? Can
we cut the cost and yet improve the service?
Our present executives do no more than they
have to do. How much more might be done by
half the number working with twice the energy
over a longer lifetime! Our present handicaps
include the death wish, the desire of man to end
it all. Given new vitality, we might end this
longing for death and have people about us
whose concern would be with life. Is it too late
to save our civilisation from its decline and fall?
We have no means of knowing. What we do
know is that, given more energy, we could at
least set about it. Future historians might have
to record our failure, but they would be compelled to add that we did our best. It might be
said that at least we tried.

CHAPTER 7

Lost Vitality

Whatever their life span, whatever the height of their achievement, whatever the splendour of their flowering, all civilisations known to us have finally collapsed. They became decadent, their forces dwindled, their arts died and their cities crumbled. Why? There can be no certainty about our answer to this question. Were the causes biological? Was there a disgenic sequel to prolonged periods of war with heavy casualties? Were the best men killed in youth and was the next generation bred from the survivors, the second-line troops, the camp-followers? What actually went wrong and why? The suggestion has already been made that soil erosion may have been the basic cause. Is the answer as simple as that? We know by now that over-taxation is a feature of decadence but are we to see in that a symptom or a result? Over-taxation is plainly the cause, not the result, of a growing burden of worse than useless bureaucracy, and this would seem to be the social equivalent of the stiffening of the joints which we associate with old age. How little, however, do we really know about it! We recognise the presence of decay, but we lack the means of measurement or analysis. We are aware of the trend, but we can say little about its origin, less about its progress and least of all about its cure.

The one evident fact among our uncertainties and doubts is that the decadence of a society is at least closely associated with the individual's loss of energy. It is almost as evident that energy derives from diet and that diet is based in turn on the nature of the soil. It is essential to remember, however, that it is energy which we are discussing, not intelligence nor mathematical skill nor appreciation of poetry. There are many valuable qualities which may not, and probably do not, derive from diet. It may be true, nevertheless, that people derive their energy from the mettle of their pastures. Research may well prove that a civilisation of growing complexity will tend to remove people from their best and nearest supplies of food, leaving them to depend for their existence on the imported, the preserved and the stale. There are numberless examples in history of settled and prosperous populations being conquered by nomadic herdsmen who lived nearer to nature and further from soil erosion. From events such as these we may come to suspect that energy must tend to dwindle with each generation further removed from the countryside. This was a common belief among many past observers. Ibn Khaldun, as we have seen, attributed human energy to the avoidance of a rich diet. To this day the Spaniards seem to need very little sleep. As for the conquistadors, their energy must have been remarkable. A mere handful of men conquered a continent, but their gifts were not shared by all their descendants. The great Spanish adventure came to an end, leaving us to wonder whether it can ever be revived.

The energy goes away, the arts become sterile, policy becomes timid and the outposts are abandoned; and it is this decay which creates the vacuum into which another and more virile civilisation is drawn. As between East and West, it is clear that their periods of highest civilisation have never been simultaneous. Instead, there have been alternate periods of ascendancy, the decadence of one coinciding with the greatest achievement of the other. These alternate phases of expansion assume a military form, and we are at first inclined to see these vast movements of mankind as the overspilling of energy, the exuberance of an achievement which can no longer be kept within its original frontier. Such overspillings do undoubtedly occur. But further study may incline us to think that the vacuum is the more powerful force. For the trade routes which link the two civilisations are the pipeline along which the invasion is drawn. And failure to maintain the pipeline at one end draws the experts in from the other. One of the strongest motives for human interference is the spectacle of a fumbling ineptitude. "Oh, for heaven's sake," we burst out, "I'll do it for you!" The roof destroyed in a typhoon is not so much pushed off as sucked off, rather, by the vacuum formed in the building's lee. So the offensive begins and will continue until its force is spent.

C. Northcote Parkinson
East and West
London, 1963, pp. 4-5

When studying the offensive which one civilisation or people may launch against another, we do wrong to concentrate too much on military power. The battle is often no more than the dramatic assertion of a superiority already established, and one which extends to the arts of peace. The suction created by a progressive decay draws in a flood of ideas and inventions. It attracts all sorts of people, travellers, traders and missionaries, technical advisers and diplomatists. The actual invasion comes later or may even prove needless if superiority has been established by other means.

The offensive is only perhaps incidentally of a military kind, the campaigns being more dramatic but not necessarily more important than the in-

fluences otherwise brought to bear . . . It is easy again to attribute military conquest to a technical superiority in weapons . . . but the facts as often refuse to fit the theory . . . The technical improvements tend to come after the first victories have been won. As for the Japanese, who conquered South-East Asia by the most humdrum methods, their technical progress never took place at all. Campaigns often give dramatic emphasis to a defeat which took place before the war had even begun. And the defeatism of the one side may be more important than the confidence acquired by the other.

Ibid., **pp. 5-6**

If the nature of the first movement, as between East and West, may need some explanation, its sequel is much easier to understand. For nearly every conquest provokes an eventual rebellion. The ascendancy of one civilisation or people over another must tend to generate resentment. Hatred results from being treated, perhaps quite kindly, as inferiors. It comes to boiling point among people who have admitted their inferiority and who hate themselves for it. Sooner or later there is likely to be a revolt against what is nowadays called "colonialism": the ascendancy of one people over another.

Among those brought up in the tradition of the American or Russian revolution there is a belief in the morality of revolt as contrasted with the wickedness of imperialism. We have to realise, however, that no such contrast has ever existed. If imperialism leads to eventual revolt the revolt leads as inevitably to a new imperialism. Successful rebels who say, "One man is as good as another," go on instantly to add "and better!" — thereby announcing their own ascendancy over some other group. English rebels against Spain were quick to enforce their own rule over Ireland. American rebels against England would stand no nonsense from Mexico. The Javanese had scarcely gained their independence from the Netherlands before they began to oppress Sumatra... How could it be otherwise? The forces of resistance — whether emotional, psychological, military or economic — are left unopposed as a result of their own success. They instinctively seek new opponents as justification for their own being. Younger sons on the make do not so readily sheath their swords for lack of argument, as Henry V's successors discovered for themselves. They find another argument, and so it has always been. Ascendancy creates resistance, and resistance turns into a new ascendancy.

Ibid., **pp. 6-7**

A gigantic and clumsy engine, powered by the alternating ascendancy of East and West, must seemingly grind on. By decaying, each civilisation creates a vacuum into which the forces of the rival civilisation must be drawn. This drive creates a resistance and recovery. By the time this has gained momentum, the colonial powers have themselves decayed, creating a new vacuum where there was once a source of energy. So the piston is driven or sucked back to its previous position, ready to repeat the process. There are observers of this process who fear that the continued and perhaps accelerated action of the piston may some day destroy us all. They demand that the engine be brought to a standstill. They suggest, as did George Bernard Shaw, that people should so intermarry that all differences will disappear. But human progress in the past has not been the result of assimilation. It has been the result of friction, the brightest sparks of invention having resulted from the clash of ideas, the interaction of flint and steel. Where friction is abolished stagnation results and this tends to be short-lived. For the absence of growth and invention is itself the first sign of decay; and what fails to develop must fail to survive.

Granted then that the conflict must continue and that it serves an essential purpose, it might still be considered desirable to lessen somewhat the shocks of future impact . . . We could check the momentum of the process by slowing down and modifying the progress of decay. But this depends again upon our having learnt to recognise decay when we see it. Once we have admitted to ourselves that civilisations are liable to decay and that our own is no exception, we can begin to ask the right questions. How are we to judge whether a society, our own or another, is decadent or not? Few people realise that historical research may be quite as important as research in organic chemistry. That is nevertheless the fact, and a programme to analyse the decay of civilisation would yield results at least as valuable as might be expected from an attempt to measure the life of electronic components . . .

Ibid., p. 8

There is need then for research, and we cannot decide in advance to what conclusions that research will lead. We may assume, however, that the decay of a civilisation must be accompanied by — and may well be caused by — a lack of vitality in the individual. It is difficult, after all, to picture a society in which the individuals are bursting with energy but all the institutions in a state of decay. We must assume, therefore, that our first concern must be with the individual. If he is lacking in drive there are a number of possible causes. Of these the first possibility is a faulty diet, lacking the elements which would give him energy and including elements which are bad for health. Those dietetic problems will be discussed in the following chapters but we should be wrong to conclude that all problems are dietetic. A second cause of decay is overcrowding in the big city. Experiment has shown that even animals need privacy and that they may fail to breed under adverse social conditions. As Professor Ivor H. Mills points out, "The major factor in breakdown of animal societies is not population density but the competitive pressure," as discovered by Professors Henry and Zuckerman:

> *I suggest that the dramatic changes in society in these crucial years (1960-1975) were associated with the increasing demands on the human brain to cope with problems. Sociological evidence indicates that frequent dramatic events in people's lives are associated with the onset of depression. Depression often leads to irritability, rows at home, broken marriages, disturbed children and attempts to escape from reality by means of drugs. Human society is rapidly resembling what Calhoun called the "behavioural sink."*

> *Times,* July 10, 1975

Others take the view that population density is an evil in itself. Roberto Vacca in his famous book, *Demain le Moyen Age,* predicts that there will be an abrupt decline in civilisation between the years 1985 and 1995, due largely to overpopulation. He says that civilisation has its best chance of survival in Sweden where there are no cities of over a million people and where the density of population is only 18 per square kilometer as compared with a population density of 92 per square kilometer in France. But France is not the country in which overcrowding is at its worst.

America is one vast, terrifying anticommunity. The great organisations to which most people give their working day, and the suburbs to which they return at night, are equally places of loneliness and alienation. Modern living has obliterated place, locality and neighborhood, and given us the anonymous separateness of our existence. The family, the most basic social system, has been ruthlessly stripped to its functional essentials. Friendship has been coated over with a layer of impenetratable artificiality as men strive to live roles designed for them. Protocol, competition, hostility and fear have replaced the warmth of the circle of affection which might sustain man against a hostile universe.

Charles A. Reich
The Greening of America
1970, Penguin ed. 1971, pp. 15-16

So the loss of vitality has other causes arising from the nature of the modern city, causes which are not easy to analyse. High-rise buildings have a bad effect on old people and on children. Perpetual traffic noise is probably tiring, even when unnoticed. The concrete jungle leaves people something less than human. With the coming of industrialism people have had a certain security, but they have been left with little else. To quote Charles A. Reich again:

> *The discipline to which the worker fell subject was a harsh one. He worked long hours which absorbed nearly all his time and energy. He was cut off from fresh air, nature and beauty, and confined to a machine-interior. His housing was little more than an extension of the factory itself... His mind was not wanted, nor his judgement, nor his imagination. His sense of design, of rhythm, of music, of craftsmanship were rejected. Boldness, courage, leadership, fun, play, kindness, affection, had no place in the discipline of the factory or the office.*

Ibid., p. 34

This description is in the past tense, referring to the earlier days of industrialism. Pay is now higher and hours of work are shorter but the conditions are otherwise much the same.

The worker's mind and imagination were not wanted then and they are not wanted now. So we live under a certain kind of pressure and one that affects our health. It is true that the pressure is not the same for all. The man at the bench or on the conveyor belt is unknowingly frustrated because only a part of him is employed. The executive in the head office building is used more fully but is under another kind of competitive stress. The director may be under even greater stress with every chance of a nervous breakdown or heart attack. The big organisation, like the big city, places a heavy burden on all its victims, ruining the health of some and shortening the lives of others. And now we have reached the point at which the people on the payroll, whether doing executive, clerical or manual work, may be the second or third generation to be caught in the same treadmill. The decay of the individual is all too easy to explain.

Other causes of individual decay associated with the big city are lacking exercise and being overweight. Where we used to walk we now go by car. The big city offers a transport by underground railway, by omnibus or taxi. We walk only in crossing the pavement from car to office, from office to car. Taking so little exercise, we eat what the old-time ploughman would have eaten had he been able to afford it. We begin to lose the athletic figure in which we once took pride. We are now faced with three alternatives. First, we can ignore the fact that we are overweight, sparing ourselves the worry but accepting a probable reduction in our life span. Second, we can attempt to reduce our weight by eating more carefully and eating less. In doing this we might wisely follow the advice of Professor Linus Pauling who said:

> "Avoid sugar, avoid sweet desserts (except when you are a guest somewhere). Avoid buying foods that say 'sugar' as one of the contents, take a fair amount of vitamins, stop smoking cigarettes, and you'll have a longer and happier life — more vim and vigour and a better time altogether."

Forum World Features, 1974

If daunted by this prospect, we can look carefully at the third alternative. Eating and smoking as we like we can resolve to keep our weight down by taking vigorous exercise. We decide to reappear on the tennis court. We plan to play a daily game of squash or fives. We boast that we can give a game to men half our age. We remember, come to think of it, that we have known half a dozen middle-aged men whose boast was exactly that. We have not seen them recently, to be sure, but we remember how slim they looked when they were last in the club, whenever that was. Then we recall one other fact: all those elderly athletes are now dead.

Violent exercise is to be avoided by the middle-aged and so is a drastic abstinence. The rule is to eat sensibly with yogurt and fruit as well as meat and fish, consuming no more calories than are needed, and exercise moderately at the same time. One should weigh oneself once a week and see that weight in kilograms does not exceed the height in centimetres above the metre. Someone of 1.70 metres in height should not weigh more than 70 kilograms and would be healthier with weight reduced by 10 percent to 63 kilograms. For women — or at least for an ideal woman with a figure like a mannequin — the weight should be 20 percent less than the centimetres above the metre in height. For a height of 1.70 metres this would mean a weight of 56 kilograms. But the taking of regular exercise is just as important as the diet. For those whose ordinary work is sedentary — that is, perhaps, for the majority of people in the civilised world of the twentieth century — daily exercises are better than playing golf at the weekend. Some suitable exercises are given in the Appendix, but it should be understood that the rule should be to begin mildly and work up gradually to something more athletic. We may feel that doing exercises each morning is unnatural and so it is.

Remember, however, that it is unnatural to ride in a car and go upstairs in an elevator or lift. If we so arrange our lives that we have little or no occasion to walk, we must compensate for this in some other way. Exercises are best for this purpose, and sudden and unusual exertions are definitely harmful.

For many people to be out of condition is a sign of decay. Another sign is a continual demand for medical advice and treatment. On this subject Lord Ritchie-Calder had this to say before the New York Academy of Science on June 5, 1971:

> *In the coronary care unit of a big hospital modern medicine can be seen at its most telegenic. Wired up like astronauts, the heart-attack victims lie immobile, a computer monitoring their every heart beat, watching for the danger signals of another attack. As soon as a disturbance is detected, alarm lights flash and white-gowned attendants rush up the defibrillating equipment to shock the undisciplined heart back into line. It is scientific, efficient, up-to-date and life-saving.*
>
> *Or is it? Last year, in a little publicised report in the British Medical Journal, a group of British doctors described a carefully designed trial in which they compared the results of treating heart-attack patients in coronary care units and at*

home. The death rate turned out to be higher among the hospital patients. Presumably the experience of being in a coronary care unit was so frightening that it more than offset the advantage of intensive care.

That is a disturbing thought but there are others, at least as disturbing. In Professor A. L. Cochrane's original and challenging book, *Effectiveness and Efficiency: Random Reflection on Health Services*, he shows that much of what passes for science is, at best, unproven, at worst, harmful. Much of the trouble is the result, he points out, of an unconscious conspiracy between the patient who longs to be cured and the physician who is anxious to help him. The desire on either side is strong enough to banish the question as to whether the treatment will do any good. Similar myths attach to the maternity ward, as Bryan Silcock has pointed out:

For almost half a century infant mortality has been falling steadily and the number of babies born in hospitals has been increasing. Conventional medical opinion sees one as a consequence of the other, and a recent official report recommended that enough beds should be provided for all births to take place in hospital.

Professor Cochrane, in a passage which should produce some red faces in the medical establishment, shows that the committee of eminent doctors responsible for the report based their recommendation on a statistical fallacy. There is no evidence that the increased number of births in hospital is responsible for the reduction in infant mortality. And he points out that Holland, where less than one baby in three is born in hospital (in Britain the figure is more like four in five), has one of the lowest infant mortality rates in the world.

Here is a piece of medical Parkinsonism in the making. A proper trial to see whether hospital births really are significantly safer could nip it in the bud and release many hospital beds for other useful purposes.

The fact is that there can be too many physicians and surgeons, too many hospitals and too many theories. The danger, moreover, in a National Health Scheme is that people who have paid for it by compulsory contribution are often inclined to want value for money. To be consistently well seems actually wasteful. The patient may be, to that extent, an accomplice of the disease. This being so, it is not altogether surprising when we find examples showing that a shortage of physicians may lead to an actual improvement in health. On this subject

Amasov propounded his Law in Izvestia: "The more doctors the higher the death rate."

He advised people against taking medical advice over small aches and pains, which mostly cure themselves. He had only a limited belief in medicine itself, observing that for every disease cured another was created — as for example, neurosis, neurasthenia, insomnia, sclerosis, asthma and all the allergies. In proof of his Law he cited the instances of Estonia and Khazistan. Estonia had a higher proportion of medical men and a much higher death rate. In Khazistan there were fewer doctors and fewer deaths. We could also point out that when the Israeli doctors went on strike the death-rate fell in sympathy.

So physicians having a wrong attitude towards youth and aging, disease and health, often do more harm than good. But wrong attitudes are not confined to medical practitioners. We have all heard stories of the voodoo death and the death wish. Are such ideas entirely legendary? In a fairly recent article Oliver Gillie has shown that there is a direct connection between the brain and the heart. "Mental stress," he concludes, "may cause a man to die" (Times, Nov. 10, 1974). Conversely, determination may keep a man alive, as was shown by General Franco during the last months of his life. If a man has no wish to live and remain healthy, he will age and die much sooner than someone who has the will to live. P. G. Wodehouse made Bertie Wooster say, "I am the best man in a losing game." Those with enough will-power have thus the gift of survival. That is why women tend to live longer than men. The average woman has more will-power, more common sense, than the average man. Beginning with a real motive to preserve their appearance, they outlive their menfolk through sheer determination. Richard Fischer has explained that "Tiredness can be looked upon as the psychological sum of physical fatigue and boredom" (Observer, Jan. 12-19, 1975). If the fatigue is due to a lack of vitamins, it is at least as clear that boredom is due to a wrong attitude of mind. As Fisher says:

In the West human energy problems involve much more than the food we eat. The powerhouse may survive on hamburgers and coffee; but it is his psychological state that carries him through. People who are bored and apathetic may be grossly overweight because they eat to compensate.

Ibid.

Professor Mary Douglas of the University College of London has done a pioneering work on the sociology of food. One of her conclusions is that many people eat more than they need because they use food as a means of communication. As eating too much will shorten life we have here additional proof that there is a psychological side to the problem of vitality and health. We are not helped, however, by Doom Writing, of which we see a good deal. An editorial in *Newsweek*, February, 1975, p. 39, drew our attention to "The Threat of Economic Catastrophe, The Coming Depression, The Great World Crisis, A Second Ice Age, The Collapse of Industrial Society and The Cyclical Decline in Civilisation" — all the headlines with which we have become familiar. There are other pronouncements which tend to depress, like that attributed to Mr. Jim Goodson, vice-president of I.T.T. Europe Consumer Products Group, in the *Times* Business Diary of November 29, 1974:

> *He sketched out his reasonably hopeful scenario with reference to two economic laws, which he entitled Murphy's Law and O'Reilly's Law.*
>
> *Murphy's Law, he explained, stated that everything that could go wrong would go wrong. O'Reilly's Law, on the other hand, stated that Murphy was an incurable optimist.*

To those who have adopted Murphy's philosophy, we must add the further number of people who read of an ailment in the newspaper and immediately feel that they are the victim of it. Doom Writing is particularly dangerous reading for people who have a tendency towards hypochondria.

There can be no doubt that Doom Writing also plays a part in weakening our will to survive.

> *Have we really lost our confidence in the supremacy of our way of life, a confidence shared by all flourishing cultures, Pygmy, Greek or Victorian? For many people the attractive pull of western culture does seem to be weakening. Many are withdrawing from a positive participation in social life and its responsibilities; some prefer to live in an alien culture in order to avoid "crippling taxation," "conscription" or even "our appalling weather." They have moved to the outskirts of our culture, opting out in the same way as the seventh-century Maya Indians.*
>
> Robert Brian, *Times*

People who have so withdrawn from the fray are peculiarly vulnerable to boredom and early senility. It is one thing to recognise the dangers which surround us. It is quite another to conclude, as many have done, that all is lost. So far as the authors of this book are concerned, it is their belief that decadence is a very real tendency of our age. They ask, however, what we propose to do about it? Faced with that question, Jacques Soustelle, a former governor of Algeria and author of *The Four Suns*, a book about the Aztecs, proposed to call in anthropologists to prescribe for the ills of society just as physicians are called in to prescribe for the complaints of the individual. Nor can we doubt that anthropologists might prove helpful. Our own approach, however, is different. Noting that the decline of a society is at least associated with the individual's lack of energy, we ask whether something can be done to restore the vitality which has been lost. It is our belief that there is much to be done and that the time has come to do it — NOW!

CHAPTER 8

Some Theories

In 1939 and later, McCay performed experiments on rats, giving less food to some and allowing others to eat as much as they liked. The first group, although retarded in growth, lived longer than the second. Some would see in McCay's results an argument for underfeeding children. There are, however, three flaws in that reasoning. First, the results of experiments on animals do not, of necessity, apply to human beings. Second, these were laboratory animals, denied all freedom of movement. Third, these were animals not fully grown, lacking any proportion of the middle-aged and elderly. Working on rather similar lines, Comfort was able to prove that the life of a mouse can be prolonged by 50 or 60 percent if it fasts for two days out of seven. From experiments such as these some scientists have been led to believe that man's life might be prolonged by underfeeding. But such a conclusion would be false. What McCay proved was that relative overfeeding may shorten life, at any rate among caged animals who have little opportunity for exercise. There is reason to suspect, moreover, that the lives of the better fed animals were curtailed by their lack of movement and that the food given to the "underfed" group was in fact sufficient for creatures whose movement was so restricted. So there was nothing in these experiments to suggest that malnutrition can prolong life.

In 1956, at the third Colloquium on Aging, held in London, Gillman said:

We think the repair of the continuously inflicted injuries, consequent on chronic malnutrition, may be important in causing the peculiar incidence of various forms of hepatic and vascular diseases, primary cancer and premature aging in the African in the Union (of South Africa)...I feel, at the outset, that it is important to make what might sound a rather categorical statement, but one which I think nevertheless the truth — namely, that the entire biology of backward peoples in Africa, the Middle and Far East, and elsewhere in the world, differs profoundly from that of Western civilised people, not primarily because of genetic differences (which cannot easily be assessed) but rather by virtue of a host of environmental factors. It became clear some years ago to my brother and me that many of the differences in Africa, and the different disease incidence in these people, compared with that in South African Europeans, could better be understood if the reactions encountered are viewed as deviations in the "life track" or "life pattern" of the African resulting from chronic malnutrition originating in infancy if not at the time of conception.

It was becoming clear, in fact, that malnutrition is the danger and that it can well begin at birth.

Bourliére made this parallel statement in 1957:

> *Furthermore the comparative study of age changes should not be limited to the various zoological groups; but should be extended to the various human populations, especially those whose genetic constitution, nutritional status and ecological environment is so different from our Western European and North American standards. When teaching at the University of Hanoi, I was greatly impressed by the way most Tongkinese peasants age as compared to their own countrymen living in the big cities — and even more with westerners. On the other hand, the so-called aging of some primitive populations would need to be investigated before it is too late.*

It will be too late, he implied, when the primitive people have died out or else been brought into too close contact with modern life. As underdeveloped areas have become independent, moreover, there may be political obstacles to further research with every hazard created by bureaucracy or civil war. There is no reason, however, why research need concentrate on darkest Africa. As President Kennedy reminded Congress on February 28, 1963:

"The Negro baby born in America today, regardless of the section or State in which he is born, has about one-half as much chance of completing high school as a white baby born in the same place on the same day; one-third as much chance of completing college; one-third as much chance of becoming a professional man; twice as much chance of becoming unemployed; about one-seventh as much chance of earning $10,000 per year; a life expectancy which is 7 years less; and the prospects of earning only half as much."

Congressional Record
pp. 3245-3246

This data probably conveys an accurate picture, especially in defining the lower expectation of life. That is the significant fact from our present point of view and it relates, most probably, to malnutrition.

At the Sixth International Congress on Gerontology, held at Copenhagen in 1963, Torben Geil had this to say:

Under-nutrition of human beings far exceeding the so-called semi-starvation in the rat is known through prisoners in concentration camps. Danish prisoners in German concentration camps during the Second World War received a diet extremely low in calories, especially protein, and two-

thirds of them lost more than 35 percent of their weight. The vegetative, asthenic, and emotional symptoms first interpreted as signs of psycho-neurosis progressed in many cases after the prisoners had returned to Denmark and were living under satisfactory social conditions.

Subsequent studies have disclosed an unmistakable intellectual impairment which, combined with physical decay, bore witness of an accelerated process of aging.

A similar attempt was made in 1961 to investigate the subsequent health of former Norwegian prisoners who had been in German concentration camps. Of those examined 87 percent showed symptoms of cerebral atrophy, suggesting that the process of aging had been accelerated by starvation, the change being similar to those observed in old age. Here then is fresh evidence of a connection between malnutrition and the process of aging, evidence for believing that the progress of old age may be delayed, perhaps for many years, by changes in diet.

In a book written for the general reader it would be out of place to go deeply into the physiology of diet. It would be wrong, nevertheless, to omit all mention of current theory in this field. A pioneer in dietetic research is Dr. Henry Simms of Columbia University who suggested that anyone who could remain as fit as he was at the age of fifteen or twenty could, in theory, live for eight hundred years. This would depend on resisting the small infections which will kill off people of old age, and this would depend in turn on molecules not becoming tangled. He explained that at every age people have protein molecules which are the most important part of the living body and which are essential to life. In youth they are detached and free to move but they tend, as we grow older, to be tied together by cross-linkers, losing their freedom of movement and producing the sort of stiffness we associate with old age. Carrying the theory forward to another stage, Bjorksten points out that the body has a partial defence against this process because the breakdown of the protein molecules, which happens quite frequently, dislodges the cross-linkers. Unfortunately, however, this defence is insufficient. What is needed, he argued, is a dissolving substance that will dissolve the cross-linked proteins. In propounding this theory he cited the work of Dr. Henry Simms and Dr. Zinsser of Columbia University, as well as that of Dr. Rudzinska of the Rockefeller Institute, and he concluded that the dissolving process might be assisted by sufficient doses of vitamins C and E. So hopeful were the early experiments that Professor Polak predicted of the year 2000 that:

. . . elderly people will be young and stay so until their breath of life snaps. One has to realise that a comparison between the elderly people of tomorrow and the old people of today will become impossible. Not only because one will live for a hundred years, or even more, but because being old will become completely different . . .

These are interesting possibilities. In realising them, however, we have to overcome a formidable obstacle. Our medical researches are mostly directed towards the cure of specific diseases, and old age is not one of them. Many people assume, rather, that death from old age is natural, inevitable and possibly desirable. That people should mostly die between the ages of sixty-five and eighty-five is more of a convention, however, than a necessity. The process of death begins with the individual's acceptance of the fact that his life is nearly over. Making no plans for the future, he lowers his guard against minor ailments, any one of which may finally end his life. Because of this acceptance of death we direct little of our research towards finding a remedy for it. In our last battle against disease we are too often defeated before the conflict has begun. Even when relatively young we yield to illness (not consciously) as our only means of gaining a rest. As we grow older we may yield more often, and when we reach the end of what we consider our allotted life span we fairly surrender. We could be worn out. As against that, we may be yielding to convention and doing what other people expect of us. There are aids to having a longer life with vitamins C and E among them as anti-oxidants, because aging is a chemical oxidation-process. But it is also, remember, a matter of choice, an attitude of mind. We die, in part, because we have lived long enough. We live because there is more for us to do.

Come now to the outstanding work of Professor Linus Pauling, twice awarded the Nobel Prize. On the subject of possible longevity he wrote:

It is my opinion that in the course of time it will be possible to control hundreds of diseases by megavitamin therapy.

He studied the results of a person being deprived of ascorbic acid and found that it involved a deficiency in connective tissue, the tissue that is largely responsible for the strength of bones, teeth, skin, tendons, blood vessel walls and other parts of the body. This connective tissue consists mainly of the fibrous protein, collagen. There is no doubt that ascorbic acid (vitamin C) is needed for the synthesis of collagen in the human body as in the body of any other animal. Collagen differs from other fibrous proteins in having a rather larger content of amino-acid hydroxyproline. There is also evidence that ascorbic acid is needed for the conversion of proline into hydroxyproline.

Pauling points to the mounting scientific results which support the idea that vitamin C can ward off colds, provided you take enough of it. For instance, he suggests that a normal daily ration of the vitamin should be about two or three grams but if you feel a cold coming on, boost it to six or eight grams. It works. Compare this with the official recommended daily level of 60 milligrams — that is 50 times smaller than the Pauling idea.

Avoiding colds doesn't make you live longer. Pauling doesn't claim that. But the fact that vitamin C can thwart the cold virus indicates that it can help us increase our resistance to infections. And this is quite right. One of the things that vitamin C does for us is help build up the minute structure of our tissue, and it is important in repairing damaged tissues, too. One of the consequences of infections is that tissues do get damaged, and the longer they remain so, the longer will the infection persist. It is therefore very reasonable that anything capable of speeding the renewal of destroyed tissues will bring the infection to an end quicker.

More than this, vitamin C is an essential part of the body's defence system, the immune system. The soldiers of this defence system are minute cells that roam the body on the lookout for invading bacteria and viruses which they destroy as soon as they find them. These aggressive cells are packed full of vitamin C — they just don't work properly without it and an infection then has a chance to get a hold. It is therefore essential to keep the body topped up with vitamin C so that the defence system can operate at its best.

Pauling worked out how much vitamin C he thought humans needed by looking back at our primitive ancestors 25 million years ago. These creatures lived in tropical conditions, ate fruit not meat, and enjoyed the sun. The point is that their diet — of raw fruit and leaves — gave them about 10 grams of vitamin C each day. Then, as man evolved, he changed his habits and became a meat eater. Meanwhile, though, the body's metabolic need for the vitamin didn't alter, so the result is that we are all getting too little of this essential food. Unless we are prepared to spend all day eating raw fruits like our ape cousins, the only way to get enough vitamin C is from bottles.

Roger Lewin,
Forum World Features, 1974

Dr. Pauling gives almost equal importance to vitamin E. Recent research in Sweden and Canada has shown that this substance does much to improve the flow of blood through the arteries and veins. A rapid circulation of the blood is important because stagnation can produce blood clots, fatal to the heart, lungs or brain. Apart from that, the blood flow preserves healthy tissue by delivering food and oxygen and removing unwanted waste products.

While taking extra vitamins such as C and E, one thing to avoid is sugar. British researcher Professor John Yudkin showed that a high sugar content in the diet almost certainly contributes to heart disease such as coronary thrombosis, and scientists in America have since confirmed this theory. So it might be kinder to your guests if you don't offer them sweet desserts at all! And with the current shortage of sugar this is perhaps no bad thing.

Lewin, *op.cit.*

Parallel research has been devoted to the diseases which are related to aging, namely atherosclerosis, arthritis and cancer. These were discussed in the *Journal of the American Geriatrics Society* from which we learn that experiments have been carried out with rabbits, rats and human subjects for a period of five years. The conclusions are that ascorbic acid is essential for the maintenance of the physiological integrity of the arterial ground substance, that a high concentration of ascorbic acid in the blood is essential to the prevention of atherosclerosis, and that the need for ascorbic acid as an oxidation-reduction factor increases with age.

In *Nutrition Today,* Dr. Robert Hodges describes how he set about studying vitamin C metabolism in some convict volunteers in America. Two of the men unexpectedly escaped. A third, under pressure and apparently on the verge of scurvy, turned informer. When he realised the probable consequences if he ever returned to prison society he became apprehensive, tremulous and pale. Stress is a mild word for what he suffered. But what Dr. Hodges had not bargained for was that the poor fellow's rate of vitamin C utilisation — that is the amount his body consumed — leapt up to two or three times the normal amount. When he was told that he was to be released on parole, his utilisation went back to normal.

The Arthritis and Rheumatism Council of Great Britain has granted 100,000 to the cellular biology division of the Kennedy Institute of Rheumatology in London to study the usefulness of vitamin C in cases of arthritis. Conclusions to be drawn from the experimental work are somewhat technical, but vitamin C has been found beneficial in correcting the excess of tissue hydrogen as also in strengthening the walls of the sac. Dr. Linus Pauling has spoken similarly about the effect of an increased intake of ascorbic acid in preserving the integrity of intervertebral discs (and thus preventing back trouble). The journal, *Medical World News,* published in 1968 an article headed "Ascorbic Acid; an Anticancer Vitamin?" The author of this article emphasises the value of vitamin C in destroying free radicals. But the experiments of Harman Verzár and Le Compte have shown that free radicals can be a cause of aging as well as atherosclerosis. So vitamin C can be used to counteract aging in two ways; first, by completing the deficiencies and increasing the construction processes; second, by destroying the free radicals and other waste products and so diminish the effects of destruction. We can thus counteract aging by keeping the balance positive.

It will be apparent from this brief outline that a great deal of useful research is in progress. It is equally manifest that more could have been done had more resources been devoted to research in this area. While it is generally supposed that death from old age is more or less inevitable for those who have lived the average number of years, we cannot expect to see a large-scale investment in geriatric research. Governments must be made to realise that old age is a disease for which a remedy is being found. More could be done, however, to complete our knowledge in this field. Nor is this a merely charitable matter of providing comfort for the old. Our efforts should be to insure, rather, that the person aged ninety is not old at all but is still able to combine experience with wisdom and energy. Nor is this all, for the vitality which we may expect to see in those we regard as old should be as characteristic of those we now regard as young and middle-aged. Confronted by decadence, our need is for an enhanced activity of mind and body. In public life and in every other direction we need today the jet-propelled activity which we plainly lack.

But are we faced by the symptoms of decadence? Any doubters on this point are referred again to the evidence of Professor Ivor H. Mills of Addenbrooke's Hospital, Cambridge:

The permissive age produced an increase in new cases of gonorrhea under 25 years of age from 5,500 females per year in the early sixties to 12,000 females per year at the end of the decade. Over the same decade offences of drunkenness, which were originally falling, rose from 70,000 a year to more than 90,000 a year. Offences of driving under alcohol or drugs jumped from

30,000 in the mid-sixties to 55,000 in 1972 and 50 percent of these were under the age of thirty.

Illegal drug offences in Mid-Anglia rose from none recorded in 1965 to 172 per year in the early seventies. In the latter half of the sixties the incidence of young children (two to four years old) finding and swallowing tablets at home in the Cambridge area rose from approximately 10 a year to 80 a year by the end of the sixties. This coincides with the sharp rise in total prescriptions in England and Wales from 242 million per year in 1965 to 272 million two years later. In the same late sixties attempted suicide by teenage males (the same age group highly represented in the group of illegal drug users) increased by a factor of five.

Times, July 10, 1975

This is the portrait of a sick society, and the picture presented by other statistics, including those of crime and growing illiteracy, is actually worse.

It would be wrong to end even a brief reference to Linus Pauling without mentioning, and indeed emphasising, the advice he has to offer the world in three words — STOP SMOKING CIGARETTES. It would be outside the scope of this book to explain the origins of this extraordinary habit, but it would be wrong to ignore what King James I said about tobacco when the smoking habit was first established and advertised (apparently) as a cure for venereal disease.

> *Now how you are by this custom disabled in your goods, let the gentry in this land bear witness, some of them bestowing three, some four hundred pounds a year upon this precious stink, which I am sure might be bestowed upon many far better uses ...*
>
> *And for the vanities committed in this filthy custom, is it not both great vanity and uncleanliness that at the table, a place of respect, of cleanliness, of modesty, men should not be ashamed to sit tossing of Tobacco pipes, and puffing of the smoke of Tobacco one to another, making the filthy smoke and stink thereof, to exhale athwart the dishes, and infect the air, when very often men that abhor it are at their repast? Surely smoke becomes a kitchen far better than a dining chamber, and yet it makes a kitchen also often-times in the inward part of men, soiling and infecting them with an unctuous and oily kind of soot, as hath been found in some great Tobacco takers, that after their death were opened. And not only meat time, but no other time nor action is exempted from the public use of this uncivil trick; so as if the wives of Dieppe list*

*to contest with this nation for good man-
ners, their worst manners would in all
reason be found at least not so dishonest,
(as ours are) in this point. The public use
whereof, at all times, and in all places, hath
now so far prevailed, as divers men very
sound both in judgment and complexion,
have been at last forced to take it also
without desire . . .*

*But herein is not only a great vanity,
but a great contempt of God's good gift,
that the sweetness of man's breath, being a
good gift of God, should be wilfully corrupted by this stinking smoke, wherein I
must confess, it hath too strong a virtue:
and so that which is an ornament of nature,
and can neither by any artifice be at the
first acquired, nor once lost, be recovered
again, shall be filthily corrupted with the
incurable stink, which vile quality is as
directly contrary to that wrong opinion
which is holden of the wholesomeness
thereof, as the venime of putrefaction, is
contrary to the virtue of preservation.*

*Moreover, which is a great iniquity,
and against all humanity, the husband
shall not be ashamed to seduce thereby his
delicate, wholesome and clean complexion-
ed wife, to that extremity, that either she
must also corrupt her sweet breath there-
with, or else resolve to live in a perpetual
stinking torment.*

Have you not reason then to be ashamed, and to forebear this filthy novelty, so basely grounded, so foolishly received and so grossly mistaken in the right use thereof? In your abuse thereof sinning against God, harming yourselves both in person and goods, and taking also thereby the masks and notes of vanity upon you: by the custom thereof making yourselves to be wondered at by all foreign, civil nations, and by all strangers that come among you, to be scorned and condemned. A custom loathsome to the eye, hateful to the nose, harmful to the brain, dangerous to the lungs, and in the black stinking fume thereof, nearest resembling the horrible Stygian smoke of the pit that is bottomless.

A Counterblaste to Tobacco, 1604

Were we concerned with smoking merely as a social habit and a personal extravagance we might conclude the argument at this point saying that the case for the prosecution rests. But King James omitted the clinical detail which is needed to carry conviction in a more scientific age. Nor did he remark, in the words of a more recent commentator, that to kiss a smoker is to lick a filthy ashtray. He could forbid smoking at his own court, however, and subsequent monarchs were to do the same. But his further steps to discourage the practice were to have an unfortunate result. He raised the tax on tobacco from 2d. to 6s. 10d., intending to discourage the dirty habit. The result, unfortunately, was to give his government (and every subsequent government) a vested interest in the tobacco industry. By 1960 the duty on tobacco stood at 64s.4d. per lb., and was effectively raised to 70s. in 1961. No government will readily forego so big an item in its revenue. In some other countries, Russia included, the smoking of tobacco was made illegal but these prohibitions were ineffective. It seemed that the habit of smoking had come to stay. No gentleman smoked in eighteenth century France or Britain — he took snuff instead — but smoking became fashionable at the time of the Crimean War. Cigarettes largely superseded cigars and pipes after about 1920 and women took to smoking them. Children were still discouraged from smoking but with only partial success. Cigarette smoke was everywhere.

Little concern was expressed about the smoking habit until 1939, the year in which Dr. F. H. Muller of Cologne suggested that it might be a cause of lung cancer. The idea was taken up again by the Americans Wynder and Graham in 1950 and made the subject of a study by the British physicians, Dr. Doll and Professor A. B. Hill, also published in 1950. Basic to their research was the discovery that lung cancer in

England and Wales which killed 309 men and 191 women in 1920, had increased so as to kill 2,258 men and 864 women in 1950. Doll and Hill showed that the death rate from all causes (per thousand) was as follows:

Age	Non-Smokers	Smokers 1-14 per day	15-24 per day	25 plus per day
33-44	1.1	1.56	1.55	4.41
45-54	3.7	5.56	7.18	10.18
55-64	12.0	17.69	20.37	25.57
65-74	31.7	47.10	42.09	59.82

They concluded that while a non-smoker aged 35 has a 15% chance of dying before he is 65, a heavy smoker has a 33% chance of so dying. These warnings had some effect on the public and more on the Ministry of Health, which issued a warning to the public in 1954. Newspapers, which carry cigarette advertisements, gave minimal publicity to the risks of smoking, and Dr. Russ published *Smoking and Its Effects* in 1955, showing that the case for smoking as a cause of lung cancer had never in fact been proved. He was perfectly right. It had been possible to show that the smoking habit and the incidence of lung cancer had both increased over the same period of years. The figures, it might seem, were significantly related, at any rate in Britain. As against that, however, the same period had seen a number of other trends; one, for example, being an increase of air pollution in cities. The coincidence of tendencies did not show that any one was the cause of any other. Nor was it certain which of them was cause or effect. Did lung cancer result from smoking or did people with lung cancer turn to smoking for relief? To prove the causal connection between smoking and lung cancer it would have been necessary to discover the precise damage done by tobacco smoke and the relevance of this to the causes of carcinoma. This had never been done. Worse still, the causes of cancer were (and are) more or less unknown. Worst of all, from the point of view of the argument, was that the figures from Britain, which pointed so clearly to a plausible conclusion, were quite different in other countries and pointed in other directions. Lung cancer was worst in Britain, with comparable figures for Finland, Austria, the Netherlands and Belgium. There were relatively few cases of lung cancer in Japan, Norway and Sweden. But the sales of tobacco did not follow the same pattern or support the same theory. Physicians, many of them being tobacco addicts, were free to believe whatever suited them best. Later again in 1963, there appeared a significant book called *Common Sense about Smoking* by C. M. Fletcher, Harvey Cole, Lena Jeger and Christopher Wood. This began the process of drawing a sensible conclusion from all the facts then known and all the theories then under discussion.

What has emerged from this and from other works on the subject is that smoking is a deplorable habit for other reasons. Whatever the truth about lung cancer and its causes, it was perfectly well established that heavy smokers often develop a persistent cough. Among manual workers this often leads to bronchitis from which non-smokers are relatively immune. When *Common Sense about Smoking* was published, there were, each year, six thousand deaths from bronchitis among men of working age. All or most of them were hastened by the effects of tobacco smoking. A similar connection seemed to exist between smoking and coronary heart disease, from which 20,000 people die each year, deaths among smokers being two and-a-half times more numerous than among non-smokers. When the annual death rate is compiled for men between 35 and 64 it is apparent that coronary heart disease is twice as dangerous as lung cancer and that bronchitis is not all that far behind.

> *It is sad to think of 1,600 unnecessary funerals of men under the age of 50 every year (44 per day) due to cigarette smoking.*
>
> *Common Sense about Smoking*, p. 38

It is not merely a story, however, of premature deaths. There is also the loss of production due to illness, quite as important (and often more important) than the losses due to industrial dispute.

> *Every working day in this country nearly a million people are away from work through illness. The annual loss is about 200 million days...In the course of a year 27 million days are lost through bronchitis...If 20% of the time lost in industry through bronchitis can be attributed to the effects of smoking, then this aspect of smoking alone causes as much economic damage as all the strikes that take place each year.*

> *Common Sense about Smoking,* p. 69

While 30% of smokers suffer from persistent coughing, only 8% of non-smokers are affected. That this condition is often preliminary to bronchitis is fairly widely accepted.

If there are doubts about the causes of lung cancer there can be no doubt about the appalling waste of money involved in smoking. Back in 1963 the British public was already spending about 1,250 million on tobacco: 20s.6d. per week for the average household, something like 7% of consumer spending as a whole and more than was spent on fuel, light, furniture and floor covering together. But the public cost does not stop there because of the fire risk. Fires indoors, caused by smoking, numbering 4,440 in 1956, had reached a total of 6,940 by 1959. Of outdoor fires one in eight is attributed to smoking. For a fraction of all this expenditure on more or less poisonous substances, people could be provided with sufficient vitamins to regain and keep their vitality. Recent research has shown that certain nutrients, vitamin C, thiamin and cysteines, can provide some protection against the toxic substances found in cigarette smoke. This is true, no doubt, but the better and cheaper plan is to avoid poisoning yourself in the first instance. Tobacco is a drug like any other and is supposed to steady the nerves of people living under stress. But drugs offer no permanent solution to any problem. Stress, where it exists, can be reduced by changes in diet and outlook. The time has come to rid ourselves of the notion, often presented in fiction or drama, that a hero needs a cigarette. His real need is to grow up and put aside such childish things. The cigarette is said to be a useful aid to conversation, a valuable device for people who do not know what to do with their hands, a help in making acquaintance with a stranger. All this may be true but these are the needs we should outgrow. Nothing that tobacco can do for us will ever make up for the health risk, the dirt, the pollution and the expense for which the smoking habit is responsible.

CHAPTER 9

Le Compte's Law

Of the joint authors of this book, one is a Belgian physician whose early experience, already described, was in the Congo. He was convinced, even as a schoolboy, that health depends among other things on eating vegetables and fruit. This interest he retained as a student, and his doctoral thesis dealt with the value in medicine of vitamin C. After qualifying, he went to the Congo in 1954 and spent the next three years in West Africa. The experience he gained there was to be very important in his career. As it happens, the other co-author of this book, an English historian, went out to the University of Malaya in 1950 and did not leave Singapore until 1958. For him, too, the experience gained overseas was to be very important. It would be fair to ask why. The answer must be that the scholar or scientist who goes to work in a developing or nascent country is at once deprived of all or most of the resources upon which the research worker in Europe can normally rely. The medical man who would normally have the help of radiologists, pathologists and chemists, who would ordinarily look to a teaching hospital for laboratory services and specialists' advice, will find himself working alone. In much the same way an historian who has depended in the past on major national libraries and archives will discover that he must now write and teach without any such assistance. In such circumstances the man thus left to his own devices must begin to use his brains.

Deprived of most normal facilities and placed in charge of a leper hospital, many men might have said that the task was hopeless. A few would have sunk into apathy and more, perhaps, would have resigned. For those more resolute, the situation provides a challenge. While the time has come for a man to use his brains, it is still truer to say that he must use his imagination. The medical co-author of this book reached this conclusion rather swiftly, encouraged by reading G. K. Chesterton's remark that "Imagination does not breed insanity. Exactly what does breed insanity is reason." Faced with his leper colony, Dr. Le Compte had no medical colleagues, no laboratory facilities and (incidentally) no electricity. So scanty was the provision of instruments that he was reduced, on occasion, to using a potato-peeler and a shoe-horn. He found himself having to perform over a thousand operations a year, but in three years lost only two of his patients: one a day-old baby from a total intestinal eventration and the other a week-old case of strangulated hernia. What was the secret of this success? He assumed that all his patients were undernourished and performed no operation until the patient's strength had been built up by doses of vitamin C and other nutrients, as for instance, protein with milk-powder. When he finally returned to Europe, he was convinced that the medical practitioner needs more imagination than he often seems to possess and less scientific equipment than he often seems to demand. Summarising his views he said, "The fewer the technical aids the better the medicine." He also took comfort in the view expressed by Sir Thomas Lewis that a doctor recognises a heart disease in the same way that a man recognises the bark of his own dog at night. He was then relieved to discover that many eminent physicians had already come to very much the same conclusion.

In 1965, Professor De Busscher conducted a symposium at the University of Ghent. He began his opening speech by saying, "The main thing is always to display three qualities which are inseparable from real medicine, old or new: hoᵢ ᵤsty, selflessness and common sense." He was strongly supported by his co-worker, Anne Remouchamps, who claimed that when doctors reduced their patients to numbers, then medicine had taken an unbelievable step backwards. Professor Marvin, past president of the American Heart Association, said the same thing: "It is unfortunate and deplorable that many physicians have elevated laboratory reports virtually to the level of infallibility." He gave examples of patients whose laboratory results suggested a serious heart condition when the fact was that they did not even have to stay in bed. All agreed that laboratory reports could be misleading and dangerous when placed in the hands of people without imagination. Common sense is more important than knowledge. In the *Times* of July 5, 1973, there was an article about "Einstein, the Modest Genius." One of his biographers, Banesh Hoffman, professor of mathematics at the City University of New York, wrote: "In essence, you know, he wasn't a laboratory man at all: he always said that there was no logical path to a great scientific discovery — the mind has to make a jump, much like that of a great painter or poet." It was said of the great French painter Matisse: "Now every fool can see that Matisse was a genius, but in the beginning it took a genius to see that Matisse was no fool." Writing in the *Lancet* of December 7, 1974, Professor P. S. Byrne concluded that the most important qualities required of the physician are humanity and imagination. The late Professor De Groot emphasised that the successful scientist must have human qualities as well. He was a histologist, but he found that even poetry was useful to him. Some of his colleagues may have laughed at him behind his back but he was right. To have imagination means to combine a sense of reality with common sense, a sense of humour with a feeling for poetry. It means, above all, to have a sense of the relative value of everything.

While in Africa, as medical director of the hospital in Kuimba, in fact as the only physician who also had to be the pediatrician, the geriatrician, the psychiatrist, the obstetrician, the surgeon, the ophthalmologist and the laboratory specialist, Dr. Le Compte noticed that his patients had a very unequal expectation of life. White men lived longer than blacks and some blacks lived much longer than others. There were a dozen genetic and environmental causes which might have been relevant, but he concluded that the rapid aging of the blacks was due to malnutrition. They were underfed and had been underfed for generations. The result was that they sickened more easily, aged faster and died sooner. There were more prosperous blacks, on the other hand, who earned enough money to buy food and were not dependent on what the jungle provided. So he drew up a table as follows:

A. NATIVES		B. EUROPEANS
ORDINARY BLACKS	RICH BLACKS	NORMAL EUROPEANS
Extremely rapid aging	Less rapid aging	Normal aging
Extreme shortage of body-building substances	Fewer and lesser shortages	Latent shortages?

From this table he deduced Le Compte's Law: aging proceeds more rapidly where the deficiencies are greater and more numerous.

His findings were supported by those of Bourliére in Indochina and of Gillman, J. and Gillman, T. among the South African natives. There could be no doubt that malnutrition was the cause of premature aging among natives in the Congo and elsewhere. But this conclusion led at once to a further question: if aging in Africa is caused by malnutrition, cannot the same be said of aging in Europe or the U.S.A.? Returning to Europe in 1957, Dr. Le Compte widened his studies. He knew that exceptional longevity is known in certain parts of Pakistan, in Hunza, in the Caucasus and in the Andes. He heard of the kava tree which is found in the Cook Islands of the Pacific from which the Polynesian natives drink an extract and from which kava-kava is extracted. He collated his findings with those of other scientists and produced a new graph in which African and European results were combined:

From this, his conclusion was that very premature aging is caused by serious deficiencies, that less serious aging is caused by milder deficiencies, and that what we regard as "normal" aging is due to deficiencies which have not been hitherto diagnosed. He supposed that the curve will never, in fact, reach the horizontal

GRAPH

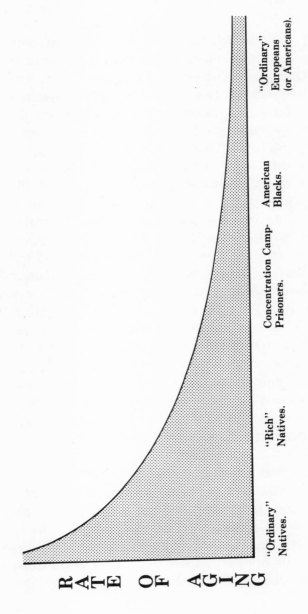

RATE OF AGING

"Ordinary" Natives.

"Rich" Natives.

Concentration Camp-Prisoners.

American Blacks.

"Ordinary" Europeans (or Americans).

line. As against that, it would seem possible to eliminate the deficiencies and prolong life for a further period of years. That is now the basis of his treatment and the object of his research.

In highly civilized countries and among fairly prosperous people there would seem to be no reason, in theory, why diet should not be adequate. In practice, the foods readily available do not contain all we need. Living the life we do in the society to which we belong, it is no longer possible to eat well and naturally. The important elements are not there or else have been ruined before the food reaches us. Moreover, we are not the first generation living under artificial conditions, far from our sources of supply. To take vitamin tablets orally is a remedy, to some extent, for the poor quality of normal food, but it would not seem to be enough. To make certain that the vitamins are actually absorbed, the only way is to have them injected. This is Dr. Le Compte's practice and it is an extension of his Law. His method is to combine the injections, intramuscular and intravenous, with the taking of tablets. His patients are then advised to give up smoking, avoid eating sugar and take regular exercise. On these principles he has cured many people who were ill and improved the health of many who had been mildly unwell. It is probable that many of his patients will live longer than they would otherwise have done.

There is no doubt that Dr. Le Compte can point to some remarkable results. One patient who had been bald for some years came to him in January, 1974 (see photograph A). He was treated with vitamin tablets, with injections and with external application of powder from the henna tree (a remedy Le Compte had learnt from his gypsy patients). By September, 1974, the patient was going to the barber for a haircut once a month (see photograph B). Now years later (photograph C), he has still more hair! Another patient was aged 67 and had already retired from work. After concentrated treatment, he recovered his health and energy, is fully employed as a journalist at the age of 90 and devotes his spare time to learning Russian.

Nor did Le Compte neglect himself or his family. Following his own advice he takes vitamins regularly and appears to be a bundle of energy, working hard at his geriatric practice, editing the journal, *Rejuvenation*, corresponding with every other practitioner in his field and filling up what time he has left by studying to qualify as a lawyer. He and his wife have nine children. Mrs. Le Compte is a well-known sculptress whose work has often been exhibited, and she has remained sufficiently young and attractive to be mistaken, at times, for Dr. Le Compte's daughter. Nor are these startling results confined to human beings. Le Compte was approached once by the owner of a

Photograph A

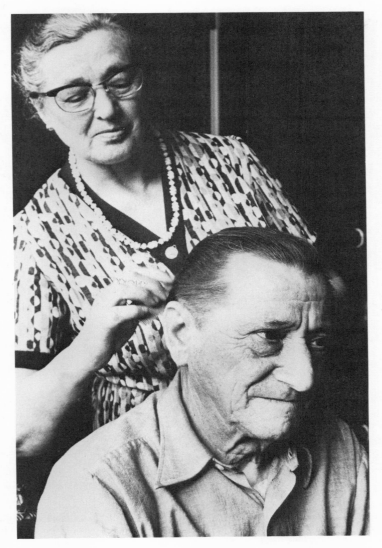

Photograph B

Photograph C

racehorse which always came in last. He made up a prescription of vitamin C, brewer's-yeast, grape-sugar and proteins which was added to the horse's food, with apparently miraculous (if slightly unethical) results.

To convince the world at large about the efficacy of a certain line of treatment, one should clearly have some pages of statistical proof. So many people were ill and this percentage of them are cured. So many were crippled and this number of them can walk. So many were old and now feel young again. It is unfortunate that Le Compte can collect no statistics in this precise form. Patients come to him suffering from general fatigue and depression. After treatment they are more optimistic and active. But to what extent has the improvement been brought about by the treatment and how much by Le Compte's dynamic personality? From a statistical point of view these results are hardly measurable. Least of all can proof be offered of a longer life span. If patients treated since 1960 are to have longer than average lives we shall have no proof of it until, say, 1990. Nor is it very easy to prove of a patient aged eighty-five and still active that he would have died (without treatment) some ten years before. If not in statistical form, however, we have a great many cases to which we can point; cases of people whose condition was hopeless and whose vitality has been recovered.

Photograph D

And if these examples are insufficiently vivid, we can point in the last resort to the Le Compte family (see photograph D). The children are the picture of health and the parents none the worse for the efforts of bringing them up. The energy and the talents of these children are quite impressive and that of the parents extraordinary.

A further difficulty about assessing the results of Le Compte's treatment derives from the fact that while science may often be (relatively) simple, the practice of medicine is not. Few of Le Compte's patients will explain to him that they are generally unfit for their work. Fewer still will complain that they are likely to die at seventy but would rather live until they are ninety. The majority will have some specific complaint like arthritis in the hands or pains in the back. Of the elderly it is true that many have a more vague story to tell, one commonly centred upon fatigue, and these can be helped by removing deficiencies in diet.

In other cases, however, the treatment must have a double purpose: to cure a specific complaint and improve the general condition. There is no very satisfactory way of reducing such records to a statistical result. We can only assert that many patients have benefited from Le Compte's treatment. When attempts have been made to have his practice made illegal, on the grounds that he has sought too much publicity, there has been a public outcry. Loudest in his defence have been patients who owe a great deal to his devotion and skill. As these multiply and flourish, showing vitality when others of the same age are bedridden, it will gradually become apparent that he has made an important discovery. But the road of the innovator is stony and uphill. In the words of one eminent thinker, James Williams:

> *First a new theory is attacked as absurd; then it is admitted to be true, but obvious and insignificant; finally it is seen to be so important that its adversaries claim that they themselves discovered it.*

That this will be the fate of Le Compte's discoveries is more than probable. In the meanwhile he meets with some opposition from other physicians and has been criticised for making exaggerated claims. He finds encouragement, however, in the history of medicine. There is no other branch of science in which the leading exponents have been so completely and repeatedly wrong. The explanation of this is simple enough. The physician discovers that he is expected to be infallible. If he appears uncertain of himself, doubtful in his diagnosis, his patient loses confidence in his medical adviser. As this confidence is important to the success of the treatment, the physician professes a certainty that he may not feel. He decides promptly and firmly that the patient has a certain ailment for which a certain treatment is known to be appropriate. In this there is relatively little harm. The diagnosis may be incorrect and the treatment may be irrelevant, but most patients recover in the end, and there is no reason why the physician should not claim the credit for it.

The danger begins when the physician comes to share the patient's belief in medical infallibility. The victim of his own propaganda, he assumes the correctness of his own views, becoming increasingly pompous and self-satisfied. This presently comes to affect the physician's relationships with his pupils, his juniors and colleagues. He becomes dogmatic and harshly critical of any medical man who ventures to disagree with him. The growth of medical intolerance is all very human, all very easy to understand, but it is remote from the humility with which the true scientist approaches his subject of investigation. To the historian of science or medicine it is obvious that the chief obstacle to progress has never been the professor's ignorance. The obstacle has always been the professor's belief that he knows it all already. Geriatrics is not taken too seriously by the leaders of the medical profession, and Le Compte's views are liable to be classed as heretical. That is not to say that they are wrong. They are in fact worse than wrong; they are inconvenient.

Dr. Le Compte has a sharp eye for professional self-satisfaction. He sees it in the mandarins of the clinical laboratory. They are too absorbed, he considers, in technique and technical aids, in laboratory tests and accepted doctrines. Looking at what they have been taught to see and recognising what they have been taught to expect, they fail to see other symptoms which may in fact prove more important. But if the men of the clinical laboratory are in some ways dangerous, the men of the research laboratory are a great deal worse. Clinical laboratory reports can be controlled by common sense. They can be adapted to our general observations. In the last resort, they can be ignored. But research laboratory results are potentially more dangerous, being more difficult to control. If members of the research staff lack imagination and common sense — and specialists in arteriosclerosis have already been compared with blind people trying to describe an elephant after touching the part of it nearest to them — we are in trouble. A person without imagination cannot readily believe that there may be a connection where he sees none. While meaning well, the scientist can be a menace.

At the other end of the scale there are quacks who offer to rejuvenate people by magic injections and pills. It might seem that they present a complete contrast to the scientist. In fact, however, their fault is the same: a lack of imagination. Something can always be done for the old by care and kindness, and even by showing an interest in them, an interest they may not have experienced. But results achieved this way are not the same as we gain by real medical treatment. There is a middle way between the way of the quacks and the way of the mandarins, and the good physician is the man who finds and follows it.

Le Compte's First Law was published in the *Zeitschrift fur Alternsforchung* in 1965: "Aging proceeds more rapidly where the deficiencies are greater and more numerous." This discovery had led him to the conclusion that old age, as a condition, is not an inevitable cause of death. It is rather an illness for which the cure may — and probably does — exist. He went on from there to consider other aspects of the subject. In his reading he came across Parkinson's Third Law: "Expansion means complexity, and complexity, decay." As originally written and published this was applicable to political science and business administration, but Dr. Le Compte noticed that the words used and comparisons made were applicable to gerontology:

> *When a tree decays it is not normally from sickness and never (one assumes) from sin. It decays because it has reached its maximum growth, maintaining that size*

and weight for the period usual with that
type of tree. It cannot live forever in any
case. Institutions, whether political or in-
dustrial, are not essentially different. For
them too, maturity leads to decay.

Parkinson
Inlaws and Outlaws
U.S. ed., 1962, p. 232

If complexity causes decay, simplicity should prevent it. Le Compte knew that unicellular creatures have an apparently unlimited life span. Weissman, Loeb and Verworn were able to keep unicellular creatures alive indefinitely by changing their nutritive medium from time to time. On this subject Verzár reports that "in a certain sense the cells don't die, but live on as colonies indefinitely, as long as favourable living conditions exist." Metabolic products prevent further cell division by cross-linking between the molecules, so that the culture medium should be changed if the culture is to live. These experiments, and those of Carrel, prove that the simpler the organism the less susceptible it is to aging, whereas the more complicated the structure of a living organism the more subject it is to aging, decay and death. According to Verzár the cells do not die but survive indefinitely as long as conditions are favorable. For a unicellular creature favourable conditions mean the replacement of deficiencies and the removal of waste products.

For man the problem of survival is not as simple. We can check the process of aging by supplying the wants in time, but we shall eventually age and die, because we cannot forever remove the waste products of metabolism. That these waste products are a cause of aging has been explained by Verzár, who attributes aging to the increase of cross-links in the collagen fibres. According to Bjorksten this is a tanning process by the waste products of metabolism. Considering all these theories and comparing them with the results of his own experimental work, Dr. Le Compte concluded that the essential thing is to keep the metabolism positive. He found himself in argreement on this subject with Dr. Joseph W. Still, who points out that few people look after themselves properly. They take too little exercise, they eat, drink and smoke too much and their physical decline begins in their early thirties. As for the intellectual decline, that may begin when they leave college:

My observations convince me that the reason so many decline is that they allow their curiosity and imagination to be stifled. Consequently in a short time most of the "facts" they memorised become ob-

solete and so, of course, they fail. Unfor-
tunately too many of these failures reach
high places in business and government
before their ignorance and lack of common
sense has been exposed.

Rejuvenation, 1975

If people live and eat and exercise wisely, they will pass through a memorising phase in childhood, pass on to a creative phase in youth and early middle age and so reach, finally, the age of philosophy (55-60 and older). By this age, unfortunately, many people have so ruined their health by unwise habits in diet or by lack of exercise that they have become useless. There is nothing inevitable about this process. To quote Dr. Still again:

...Animals do not decline greatly in
physiological functions until true senility
sets in. The same is true of those people
who protect their bodies from abuse and
who maintain their health and vigor by in-
telligent use. In those who avoid excessive
harmful stress, the rate of decline in bodily
functions is equally slow and actual senili-
ty is usually only a terminal event, lasting
only a few months...

Le Compte's Second Law was an extension of his First and resulted from his contact
with gerontologists throughout the world. Hav-

ing established that the aging process might be hastened by deficiencies, Le Compte came to the further conclusion that it is caused by deficiencies in the first place. His Second Law is therefore as follows: aging is caused by deficiencies. It was first published in *The Journal of the American Geriatrics Society,* Vol. 14, No. 4, 1966. This discovery has been widely accepted, as for example by Bjorksten. It was also acclaimed by Komarov in a lecture given before the Soviet Presidium of the Academy of Sciences in January, 1976. The importance of this discovery lies in the fact that until 1966, there had been in the whole history of mankind only about twenty theories of aging worth considering. Of these the first dates from the reign of King Solomon, whose aging was attributed at the time to loss of heat. Later theories suggested a loss of vitality or loss of vital force. These ideas are not especially helpful, but they resemble each other significantly in agreeing that there is a deficiency of some kind. This would seem to be the fact: the symptoms of aging include a defect or loss, as of hearing or sight. If basic deficiencies were made good, aging would not occur.

Le Compte's Third Law was published in *Geriatric Times,* Vol. III, No. 5, 1969. So far, according to Le Compte, geriatricians have studied the treatment of elderly people. He maintained that geriatrics should not be the science of treating the elderly; it should be the science of preventing the process of aging. This can be done in two ways: by restoring the deficiencies and removing the waste products. To restore the deficiencies is relatively simple, but it was for long a question whether anything could be done about the waste products. Thanks now, however, to the experiments of Harman and Komarov, the dividing line between the unicellular and multicellular is no longer so absolute. It has been found that the waste matter of the metabolism can be destroyed in the organism by products such as Harman's butylated-hydroxy-toluene or Komarov's hydrogen sulphide. Instead of removing the waste products we can destroy them. In this way the multicellular organism can also survive indefinitely. The ratio of construction and destruction can thus be kept positive; and aging, the metabolism disease, can be overcome. So Le Compte worded his Third Law as follows — by keeping the metabolism positive forever, we gain perpetual life.

He was encouraged to reach this conclusion when he realised that C. Northcote Parkinson, working quite independently, had come to a rather similar conclusion, which he worded thus — youth is a possession you can keep if you choose.

From reading Le Compte's three laws one may be tempted to conclude that the problem of aging has been solved and that those now living can live for centuries. Le Compte himself has dared forecast a possible life span of a thousand years, being struck off the Belgian register for his pains — and nominated, incidentally, for the Nobel Prize. But human problems are not that easily solved. Three further obstacles stand between man and a greater longevity, and we need to know what they are.

First of all, there is official opposition. Governments do not respond very happily to the suggestion that their rule is associated with a period of decadence. Politicians prefer to see themselves as standing on a summit of human achievement, reached by centuries of effort. If anything is imperfect this is clearly the result of the recent misrule of their opponents. Under enlightened rule, perfection has been (or soon will be) attained. They do not readily vote money for research into the causes of decay. And something of the same attitude prevails among members of the medical establishment. They regard new ideas with apprehension and distrust — the more so when put forward by physicians whose love of conformity is not (at first sight) too obvious. There is much research being done, but more is wanted and progress is held back by lack of encouragement and by active opposition. This is a feature of the history of medicine, no more characteristic of this age than of any other, but it will inevitably delay the process by which a theoretical solution comes to be practically applied.

The second obstacle lies in the very nature of scientific progress. Even were there no opposition, there is an inevitable time lag between theory and practice. Leonardo da Vinci invented a flying machine, but it ended where it began, on the drawing board. A submarine was invented in seventeenth century England, to be built of wood and propelled with oars. A torpedo (of sorts) was invented in the time of Napoleon. In these and in a hundred other instances, the idea was sound but premature. The world's technology was not equal to making what the inventor had designed. Technical progress may be faster today, but the time lag remains and is unlikely to disappear. There are all sorts of difficulties we must overcome if we are to produce a new generation with an extra twenty years of life expectation. This should be possible, and as Le Compte says, "Tomorrow is built today!" So it is, but we are compelled to recognise the fact that tomorrow is not here yet. There is, one suspects, a great deal to do and all too few people to do it. The people who emerge from Dr. Le Compte's surgery may well have — and some of them have already had — a longer than average life span. But these are only an experimental handful. To extend their privilege to any considerable number of people would require an enormous effort of propaganda, persuasion and improved technology. The change in life span, highly desirable as it may be, would take many years to bring about.

The third obstacle is the most serious of the three. We are faced with problems of overpopulation. On this subject we have heard many arguments centered upon the world's food supply. Must we starve if the number becomes excessive? Can more food be produced than now seems possible? These are the themes discussed and they are all beside the point. When a zoological species becomes too numerous overcrowding its habitat, it ceases to breed, we are told, and may become extinct, not from shortage of food but from lack of space.

Mankind is increasingly under the same sort of pressure, as already noted in Chapter 7, and it has nothing to do with the food supply. The pressure is not easy to describe but city dwellers become aware of it. There may be a lack of privacy — and even animals need privacy — or there may be a lack of silence. Whatever the individual reactions, there must be a revolt of some sort against being herded together. But a sudden lengthening of the life span would initially make the situation very much worse. For a generation or so the numbers would be greater than ever. There would be other problems as well. If the top executives are to retire, as now, at sixty or sixty-five, what are they to do for the next quarter of a century? If they remain in office, how can their successors wait so long in the role of number two? And will number two be fit for promotion after being subordinate for (say) sixty years? Problems as difficult centre upon the unskilled worker. At what age is he to retire? And what is he to do with himself during a retirement lasting as long as thirty years? There may be no problem for the research scientist, but what about the janitor or garbage man? What about the widow or the actress? These are questions we need to ask and answer before plunging too boldly into a programme of life extension.

It can also be assumed that there are other complications we may not foresee. We have accepted the idea of a marriage which may last for up to fifty years. Can it last for seventy years? Should a marriage last for a limited period of years? Can we face up to having great-grandchildren around? There are many subjects on which one should have to think.

One doctrine we should have to jettison is that of human equality. As a religious belief it may have some way to go. As a practical concept it is already proving unhelpful. But what equality can there be between a man of forty and a man of ninety? We can argue today that the younger man's energy must be weighed against the older man's experience. So indeed it can, but what if the older man has retained his energy? Given the new situation, the idea of equality becomes ludicrous and untenable. We should also be driven to concede that intelligence is largely hereditary, which it obviously is. Our notions of equality derive from a shortish life in a quickly changing suburban community; we don't believe in heredity because we never see it. But if five generations could be seen at once — as happens, say, with pedigree dogs? Then the importance of breeding becomes so obvious that we wonder whether it should any longer be left to chance. We must assume, then, that a longer expectation of life could lead to a massacre of our more cherished beliefs. First to go would be all idea of life beyond the grave. For the young it would be too remote to be worth considering. For the old it might have lost its attraction in later life. With religion in its present form would go the dogmas of democracy and the sophistries of socialism. We should need to think again, but, luckily, we should have time for thought. It would be futile now to guess in what direction those long-term thoughts would lead.

If people are to be endowed with a longer life span, this revolution in human outlook must clearly be limited to two ways. Whatever the length of life to which men may finally aspire, it is clear that an extension of ten, or at most, twenty years, is all we could immediately handle; and that, heaven knows, will create problems enough. The goal is eminently worthwhile, but we should do best to take one step at a time. It would also be essential to extend the life of some people, not of all, if only to avoid the dangers of overpopulation. With that point agreed, we should have the difficult task of choosing those whose life is to be prolonged. Up to a point that would be easy, the full treatment being reserved for those willing to live longer. But not everyone is willing! But selection, beyond a certain point, would become difficult. And what would the reaction be of those rejected? Even now we carry the burden of mental deficiency, well represented in every legislature, but can we be expected to carry it for another twenty years? These are problems of the future and we cannot pretend to solve them now. Neither, however, can we ignore them. Once we have placed them on the agenda we can go on to consider further the ways and means by which life may be extended.

CHAPTER 10

Tomorrow Is Built Today

The idea is slowly gaining ground that our life span is very much what we choose.

There is no principle in nature which dictates that individual living things, including men, cannot live for an indefinitely long time in optimum health.

So writes Bernard Strehler, one of the best known gerontologists. Peter Medawar began research in this field at Oxford before World War II and has since written much on the subject, as also to justify the work that is being done. Arguments have been put forward against all attempts to prolong life, but Medawar points out (*Times,* Feb. 24, 1975) that all advances in medicine have tended to prolong life. There is no difference in principle between extending the life of the old and seeking to cure rheumatoid arthritis or cancer.

Little advance has been made recently in prolonging the life span, but that is not surprising. In former days a person who reached the age of sixty had to have been pretty tough — natural selection had been operating throughout life and the weaker would have fallen. There is no God-given parameter called the normal life span; the life span is what we cause it to be.

In the same article our attention is drawn to the novels of Jane Austen. In *Persuasion* we meet Sir Walter Elliot, Baronet, born in 1760, his daughters, including Elizabeth, born in 1785, and Anne, born in 1787. Neither was married when the story opens, evidently in 1814. Sir Walter still hoped, however, that Elizabeth would marry suitably.

It sometimes happens, that a woman is handsomer at twenty-nine than she was ten years before; and, generally speaking, if there has been neither ill health nor anxiety it is a time of life at which scarcely any charm is lost. It was so with Elizabeth; still the same handsome Miss Elliot that she had begun to be thirteen years ago and Sir Walter might be excused, therefore, in forgetting her age or, at least, be deemed only half a fool, for thinking himself and Elizabeth as blooming as ever, midst the wreck of the good looks of every body else; for he could plainly see how old all the rest of his family and acquaintance were growing . . .

Penguin ed., p. 38

The baronet was aged fifty-four and all about him were growing old. But what of Anne (aged 27)?

A few years before, Anne Elliott had been a very pretty girl, but her bloom had vanished early; and as even in its height, her father found little to admire in her, so totally different were her delicate features and mild dark eyes from his own: there could be nothing in them now that she was faded and thin, to excite his esteem.

Ibid., p. 37

If the girl might have lost her looks by the age of twenty-seven, a man of thirty-five could be regarded, at least by the young, as practically senile, or so we learn from *Sense and Sensibility:*

[Colonel Brandon]...was silent and grave. His appearance, however, was not unpleasing, in spite of his being, in the opinion of Marianne and Margaret, an absolute old bachelor, for he was on the wrong side of five-and-thirty; but though his face was not handsome, his countenance was sensible and his address was particularly gentlemanlike.

p. 29

When it is suggested to Marianne that the Colonel may be in love with her, she thinks the idea absurb.

But at least, mama, you cannot deny the absurdity of the accusation, though you may not think it intentionally ill-natured ...he is old enough to be my father; and if he were ever animated enough to be in love, must have long out-lived every sensation of the kind. It is too ridiculous! When is a man to be safe from such wit, if age and infirmity will not protect him?

Marianne is no sufficient witness to the accepted ideas of her period, but we may perhaps agree that the expectation of life was less. Jane Austen was forty-two when she died and had gained by then a lifetime of experience. We have come to expect a longer life than that.

A recent and important comment on this subject was made by Professor S. Timmins of the Berkeley campus of the University of California. Speaking at the World Gerontological Congress held in Israel in 1975, she put forward the view that:

... specific dieting manipulations can influence physiological aging through their effects on brain monamines ...and that alterations in the levels and metabolism of these substances may stop the action of a biological clock governing both growth and aging.

She ended by expressing her belief that

the whole subject warrants intensive and continuing study.

It is Linus Pauling, however, who has defined the target. He argues that by eating the right food and taking extra vitamins we may expect to live for an additional twenty years. Much depends, however, on the age we have reached when we begin to improve our dieting habits. The sooner we change our regimen the better will be our chances of a longer and better life. We have to realise, however, that we pay for the bad nutrition of our parents and grandparents. This is now generally admitted, but we suspect that the hereditary ill-effects of malnutrition may go back more than two generations, and may impair, for example, the efficacy of vaccination, a conclusion reached by Dr. R. K. Chandra on the basis of work done in Newfoundland on immunology and the development of antibodies. A recent publication issued by the World Health Organisation draws our attention to the "vicious circle by which malnutrition leads to disease, which exacerbates malnutrition, which further reduces resistance to disease." The authors of this publication admit that little is known as yet about how malnutrition causes depression of immunity or whether the malnutrition of the mother during the development of the foetus is likely to produce worse effects than the later starvation of the child itself.

The Agricultural and Medical Research councils have set up five working-parties, but although they have provided thorough reviews and a substantial index, there is no bibliography, summary or conclusion. Since 1967, three of these units have been closed down, only those in London and Southampton remaining active. Perhaps because of successful work during World War II, it is denied that there is any further need for a coherent policy in either basic or applied research in nutrition. In the developing countries the need is not for research but for action. This view finds fresh support in an article published in the *Lancet,* Feb. 1, 1975, which refers again to work done by the Food and Agricultural Organisations and the World Health Organisation. The conclusion reached at this high level is that a man's energies require many essential food nutrients. The World Health Organisation has published a handbook showing tables which set out the recommended amounts and main sources of these nutrients and the effects of both deficiencies and excess. The authors, while providing the information necessary for food planning, acknowledge that many basic problems of distribution, economics and education have still to be solved.

So the basic facts about diet are largely known and must colour our thought about longevity. But diet is not the whole secret. As important in this context is the attitude of mind. Tiredness is an attitude of mind, and aging results also from being increasingly tired. If we retain our health, our youth and our energy, it is at least partly because we have resolved to do it. If an improved diet takes us halfway to a healthy longevity, we cover the remaining distance by an act of will. How is this done? How do we set about it? In attempting to answer this question we may fairly assume that the reader is at least vaguely attracted to the prospect of a longer life. Were he already exhausted and hopeless he would not be reading this book at all. So a vague interest in longevity is something upon which we can initially rely. Where do we go from here?

There are several rules to observe, and the first is to relate your thought to action. We are all deluged with information about world and national events, the news being conveyed to us by television, radio and newspaper. There is a famine in India, an earthquake in Turkey, a typhoon in China, a revolution in Chile, a bank robbery in France, a riot in Italy, an aircraft crash in Germany, an assassination attempt in the U.S.A. and in Britain a football match prevented by heavy rain. News has mainly to do with disaster, because events which are pleasant to hear about are seldom sufficiently dramatic. The general effect is gloomy and our reflections are gloomier still. The twittering ineptitude of politicians — and indeed their mere appearance — leaves us dejected and without hope for the future. We can tell each other that the bomb exploded in Belfast is not really typical of Ulster life (or death) — that no bomb went off in the majority of the streets. We can reflect that the strike in the car industry is in contrast with work being resumed in the docks.

The fact remains, however, that we seldom have much cause for self-congratulation. Things could be worse, we say bravely, although we may wonder how. But all or nearly all these disasters have this in common, that we are not personally involved. Nor, in most instances, can we do anything about it. Having realised that, we should resolve to eliminate, as far as we can, all thought, and certainly all worry, that does not and cannot lead to action on our part. If someone known to us has died, we can write to the widow or attend the funeral. If the event is in some other continent, by contrast, and nothing to do with us, we had best forget about it, wasting no time on reading the details. We cannot help, we might possibly hinder, and we do well to mind our own business.

Does this represent a selfish point of view? The common sense angle is best understood by studying the opposite attitude. This is the age of demonstration, planned mostly so as to appear on television. We have become accustomed to seeing columns of unattractive people shuffling through the streets under banners relating to some wage claim. There may be nothing particularly admirable in these displays of selfishness, but we must concede that they might conceivably have some tiny influence on some negotiation. There are, by contrast, the demonstrations which do not concern the demonstrator and which can have no influence on anybody. The cause can be remote — the plight of some reputed hero in South America, the impending execution of some rebels in Spain, the alleged ill-treatment of dissidents in South Africa. As between these various grievances, the factor in common is that all protests are directed against the right (as opposed to the left) in politics, and that the demonstrators know nothing whatever about the conflict in which they seek, by gesture, to intervene. "Remember Chile" — these are the words printed on the rucksack of some fool who could not find Chile in the atlas. Protests can take every imbecile form, from ruining a football ground to preventing a cricket match. Those who take part are often "students" whose neglected studies are paid for out of the taxes. The expense of bringing them to the scene of their demonstration has been met from funds supplied by a subversive organization or indeed by some foreign power. Those against whom the procession is planned are normally unaware of the incident and will never hear of it. Nor, if they did hear of it, would they take the slightest notice. That there are fools in the world would not surprise them. This is something they already know.

A demonstration is an exercise in futility, reaching its peak of ill manners when stones are thrown at an embassy's windows. Since the dawn of history the person of an envoy or herald has been regarded as sacred. Under the proper flag he can safely approach the enemy and return unharmed from his mission. That is the tradition, and it is based on common sense, for it is best, as a rule, to hear what the enemy has to say. That an ambassador should never be harmed is even more obvious, for by threatening him we endanger the life of our own ambassador resident in the country concerned. We must then reflect that an ambassador is not responsible for his country's policy. His task is to explain it. He did not originate the policy, and he may not agree with it. Nor will any discourtesy directed against him modify the instructions he has received. To any literate person all these facts are obvious. When, therefore, a crowd of people throw stones at the Ruritanian Embassy, we can safely assume that the rioters are more or less imbecile. As feeble-minded are those responsible for affording the television coverage which encourages, or has even caused, the riot.

Demonstrations and discourtesies are not the subject of this book, but they illustrate the folly of adopting a fervent attitude towards events which do not concern us and which we do not understand. Towards living a prolonged and active life our first rule is to take little notice of disasters and follies which are remote from us in space, time and comprehension. Thought is useful only if it leads to action. In the news, concentrate on events which are relevant to your own and your family's life. Do not worry or grieve about other incidents. Do not ponder too much about dangers which may affect the remote future. Think rather about your friends and neighbours. What can you do for them or for the town in which you live? Is there anything you can do? Is there an area in which you can exert some influence? Have you some special knowledge which might be applied? It is not suggested that you should plunge into local politics but that you should stop worrying about things which are not your concern. Thought should lead to action and where action is impossible it is better to think of something else. People can wear themselves out with worry about changes of climate to be expected in the twenty-second century. This is only possible because they are relatively idle. Their energy would be better spent in preventing the pollution of the local stream. When you are sufficiently intent on doing something constructive and useful, there is less room in your head for worry and misgiving, for dire prediction and vain regret. Your primary mistake is not in worrying but in having nothing more constructive to think about. The worst mistake of all is to live in the past, revealing your attitude in phrases like "I wish I hadn't...," "If only John were still alive...," "My mistake was in buying this house...." "If I hadn't taken the wrong advice about those shares..." Here again, the error is not in expressing grief but in failing to make some other plan. Life begins now and our chief concern must be with what we do next. Has the milk been spilt? Bring in the neighbour's cat. Have beer instead of tea. Forget the disaster and turn to something else.

The second rule is to decide on a longer life, determine its minimum length and plan what use you will make of it. Suppose you are aged sixty, expecting to retire at sixty-five and die at seventy. If you give no thought to the matter, you will die most probably at sixty-five, six months after retirement. Decide instead that you mean to live until you are eighty. That gives you fifteen years after retirement. What use will you make of that time? You cannot sit in an armchair for the next decade. Unless you have a plan, there is no point in living so long. Do not plan to offer advice and aid to your grandchildren — that is not what they want or should have. No, the work you plan should be done by yourself. Over that given period you will create a garden, collect a library, build a schooner, write a trilogy, endow a theatre, or restore an ancient building.

What can be done in fifteen years of active life? You alone know what you can hope to accomplish in the time available. But if you have to reply, "There is nothing I can do — nothing I have the urge to do!" there is little point in living for long after your retirement. If you are to live long you must have an objective. For a man or woman who has worked hard and achieved success it may seem reasonable to say, "When I retire I shall have fun, I shall cruise around the world, visit all the places I have heard about, see all the shows that I have missed, eat the meals I have done without, and read the books for which I have never so far had the time." As a plan for five years, that may or may not be possible. As a plan for fifteen years it certainly will not do. A longer life implies a better plan than that. If no plan occurs to us it seems pointless that we should live so long.

The third rule is to act the part of someone whose early death would be undesirable. Few of us can say with confidence, "I deserve to live an active life until I am eighty-five or ninety. My death before then would be a disaster to the community. I must stay alive — I owe that much to mankind!" We may even question whether anyone so self-satisfied could really be of much use. We know, most of us, that we have faults and weaknesses, that we can be spiteful and unkind, that we have often been careless and idle. That our longer life may be justified is more of a hope than a certainty. How shall we set about it? What mental effort must we make? The answer is that we must pretend to be much better than we are. In the armed services a young officer is taught that he must never despair or complain, that he must never grumble about the heat or the cold, that he should never admit to being downcast or tired. When the going is hard, it is for him to set an example of cheerfulness and patience. He should be quick to encourage, and console, ready with a joke or a helping hand. He should have courage enough to share with others. He should be an inspiration to everyone else. On this subject there are words of wisdom in the novel by Richard Hughes called *In Hazard* which describes, at length, the effect of a hurricane on a 9,000 ton cargo vessel.

There was a smell of stale sea, stale food, and stale air; but there was another smell too; bitter, ammoniac. It was quite faint, but the captain knew it. You do not forget it, if you have ever smelt it. It was the smell of fear. Disciplined men can control their muscles, even their facial expressions. But they cannot control the chemistry of their sweat glands.

Captain Edwardes sniffed, and knew that the men needed some encouragement; so he gave it: his shaggy eyebrows sticking out like horns over his brilliant eyes, his tubby body like a lighthouse on a rock. For he felt himself full of power, like a prophet, with enough courage to serve out round the ship in ladles ...

... Yes, he had been worried. But that was only at first. For soon the storm reached such a height that plainly this was no longer an issue between himself and his Owners, but became an issue between himself and his Maker. That altered things. That suited him better. From then on, he was like an artist in a bout of inspiration.

The boys were the turning-point; when they came rushing up on the bridge, courageous in themselves and confident in him. It was they who lit him. Then, later, as the storm increased to its immense height, so the flame brightened; his whole mind and body were possessed by intense excitement. No room for thought of the Owners. No room in him for anything but a gigantic exhilaration, and a consciousness that for the time being all his abilities were heightened.

pp. 80-82

That is a fine description of how courage (like cowardice) can pass from mind to mind. The captain had "enough courage to serve out round the ship in ladles." We may few of us be as resolute as that, nor may our courage be put to that sort of test. But we can pretend to have the virtues we lack. Copying the real leaders we can imitate their attitude towards fatigue, disaster and death. In the end, if we persist in the counterfeit, we may end by turning our pretence into something more than pretence.

The Happy Hypocrite, by Max Beerbohm, is the story of the wicked Lord George Hell who roistered with the Regent, who gambled, drank and behaved very badly indeed. The dissipated life he had led was plainly shown in his face, from which children would fly in terror. Then he fell in love with a young, pure and innocent girl. It was hopeless, he knew, to approach her as he was, but he thought to save the situation by resorting to a maskmaker. He was provided with a mask which perfectly presented the face of a saint. Putting this on and changing his name to George Heaven, the former profligate approached and won the girl he loved and was extremely happy. She, too, was happy but puzzled about one thing — her lover was always serious, could never smile or laugh. One day they were having a picnic, and Lord George was accosted by a woman he had previously known and who had penetrated his disguise. She finally rushed at him, clawed at his face and tore the mask away. All seemed to be lost, and he began to make what excuses he could for his cruel deception. But no excuses were needed, for his own face behind the mask had become that of a saint, and the girl loved him more than ever. That story gives us the secret of the pretence which is eventually no pretence at all. We must form our image of successful old age, adding experience to energy, kindness to wisdom and the part of age as we have conceived it. If we act the part perfectly, ignoring a few aches and pains, undiscouraged by a few handicaps, resolved still to perform the task we have chosen, we may find in the end that our pretence has become reality.

If any of us are to live for ten or fifteen years longer than our relatives had any reason to expect we shall owe our longevity in part to medical imagination and research but also in part to a sensible diet and to added vitamins. We shall also owe it, in part, to our refusal to worry about things which do not concern us, to our careful plan of what we shall do with our extra years, and to our skill in pretending to be much wiser and better than we really are. But if people are to put up with our presence for an extended period of life, we shall owe something to their patience. Our best way of repaying this debt is to show others, by example, and precept, that they too can have longer to live. This is largely a matter of choice but there is still much to do in geriatric research. Support for this further work, and especially political support, should come first and foremost from those who are benefiting now from the work already done. We can do something by donation and bequest, more still by using our influence on the government, the legislature, the public and the press. There must obviously be appeals for funds but with the prospect in this instance of a real economy. For it is far cheaper to retain the expert you have than to replace him with a trained successor. What can be more wasteful than the relatively early death of a man whose brain and experience die with him? If there is a secret in how to grow old usefully those who have discovered it should not keep the knowledge to themselves. There is a morality in this but a mere self-interest might point to the same conclusion. For there is nothing very attractive in an extended old age which no others would share. Old men have been heard to say: "I don't want to live much longer. There is nobody left who calls me by my first name." If any of us are to live longer than has been usual we shall want others to share that privilege and responsibility. It is not a privilege, nor a burden, that we should want to bear alone. The fourth rule, then, is to share with others the secret of an extended but useful life.

What rule comes fifth? This is the rule, surely, which should prevent us from standing too much in the way of younger men. We are not to know as yet what the effect will be of some folk having a longer life. There will be problems, no doubt, which we have not foreseen. But one immediate problem must be the position of a number two serving under a number one who refuses to retire and who seems likely to live forever. Universities solve this problem by making number one a professor emeritus and thus making room for number two as the new number one. Such a device may be extended to other types of organisation. It might prove wiser, however, to make a clean break and encourage the old chief to start again in a different role. What would be fatal, one must suspect, would be to raise the retiring age to seventy-five, causing despair all along the line. We must assume, incidentally, that the older men of the future will be responsive to new ideas, but what if they are not? So there are doubts and difficulties on every side. Among high-caste Indians the tradition was that each man should pursue his trade and raise his family, thereafter dividing his old age into two periods; one to be spent in meditation and the second and last to be spent as a penniless mendicant sitting by the roadside. This solution is unlikely to be acceptable in the West and there might even be doubts about it in India if the total period were to be prolonged by fifteen years or so. There must come an end, surely, to the most profound meditation.

Come now to the sixth rule and the last. It must be understood that the old but vigorous man of the future will show only a distant interest in his own descendants. Ours is a world in which parents no longer try to influence their children after a certain age. As from about the age of graduation children are deemed to know what they are doing and they seldom welcome direction over their choice in marriage. At a somewhat later stage they may call on grandmother to look after the children on occasion and that represents what may be the final stage in parent - child relationship. But what if the parents are still active at the age of ninety? By then the generations in simultaneous existence will perhaps be four: parent, children, grandchildren and great-grandchildren, with great-great-grandchildren not impossible. Supposing, moreover, that the parents retain their virility into old age, the children born in their later years will be the contemporaries of their earlier grandchildren. One way and another, the family could be very numerous indeed. At this point, or indeed long before this point, these family relationships will have passed the breaking point. Advice from a great-grandfather might be resented and the more so if the grandfather's advice were directly opposed. The Chinese, as we know, have had in the past a great respect for their ancestors but they did not expect to find their more remote ancestors still around.

Following this change in life expectation we must expect to see some changes in the generation game. Beyond a certain point there would presumably be a tacit agreement that relationships might be ignored. For all reasonable purposes of family contact three generations would seem to be enough.

Here then are some suggested rules applicable to a world in which people are to live for another twenty years after retirement. They may at least provide us with some food for thought. We are also driven to think more urgently about eugenics. So far we have briefly discussed the size to which a long-lived family might extend. We have tacitly assumed that such a family will derive from healthy stock. We have perhaps imagined that there will be hereditary strains of ability and that the chances of producing a genius will be greatly improved. There are many attractive possibilities. We must remember, however, that the dangers are as numerous. What if the first long-lived parents were half-wits? This must obviously be the subject of careful regulation. But what if there is a strain of lunacy, undetected when the life-pattern was changed? There could then be an alarming growth of insanity. It is a question, incidentally, whether a society which is to carry a large number of living ancestors can also carry the present number of the incurably sick, insane or criminal. If some are to live longer then others must be sterilised or even eliminated.

Given a longer life (for some, not all) we must discard the concept of human equality. There can be no pretence of equality as between two men or women of equal vigour but with a fifty years difference in age. There can be as little pretence of equality between those of the same age but whose life expectation differs by twenty years. Democracy cannot long survive the revolution we are considering, for how can we fail to give greater weight to the opinion of those whose experience is so much longer? As for dictatorship, the necessary sequel to chaos, it presents a more hideous aspect if the dictator's life is to be prolonged for another two decades. It may be thought that some recent dictators lived quite long enough. What if they had ruled for as long again? The prolongation of life brings with it a host of new problems, those we have mentioned and others of which we are not yet aware. What we are discussing is a plan for revolution.

As a result of studying this book, the reader may conclude that a longer life is possible. Given a certain treatment, some people, we know, have recovered their energy and their youth. Others have been given the same sort of treatment from an early age, from birth and even (in effect) from before birth. We believe that they will live longer than other people, but we cannot pretend to know yet. After fifty years there will be more positive evidence, one way or the other. In the meanwhile, over ten years or twenty, we may hope to have evidence which will at least point to a conclusion. Over the same period more research will be done and our methods of treatment should improve. It will be agreed, in the end, that the extension of human life is possible and desirable. All this will take time, however, and this is not a subject for regret because of the problems which must arise from the change we mean to bring about. We have mentioned but a few of these and it must be apparent that a great deal of work and thought must lie ahead of us. It will not be enough to introduce an alteration in the span of life. We shall have to reshape our institutions on the basis of this change, few of them likely to be unaffected and some of them sure to be destroyed. Gaining as we should from a longer life and continued energy, we shall gain as much again from having swept away a monstrous heap or nonsense. If we are to resist, reverse or even merely retard the current process of decay, we shall have done something to save our civilisation from a new Dark Age. It is evident that time is short and that we have all too much to do.

We have considered a future age in which some difficult decisions will have to be reached. But these problems await a future generation.

For the people of today, for those who read this book, there is a far simpler choice. Do you choose to live an energetic life until you are eighty or ninety? At some future time you might have to prove that your life is worth prolonging, but here and now the choice is yours. There is no certainty about the treatment we advocate. It may not succeed with everyone and it may not succeed with you. The fact remains that it offers a chance — we believe a good chance — of admitting you to the select company of those who have rejected a relatively early death. The decision is yours and it is not an easy one. How will you use another twenty years if given them? Unless you have a quick answer to this you would do better to settle for a shorter life. It would be perfectly rational, in that case, to live as you have lived, overeating and overweight. If you cannot live without sugar and tobacco then you are perfectly entitled to smoke and die. As the reader of this book, however, who has more or less reached the end of it, you will at least be making a deliberate choice. You can choose between the possibility (not the certainty) of a longer life and the likelihood (not the certainty) of a life which is relatively short. It would be quite wrong to think that all the advantages are on one side. For anyone with a great work before him the choice is easily made. For anyone who is dying to smoke, the choice is no more dif-

ficult. For the rest of us, for the majority, the
advantages have to be weighed against the
drawbacks, and the choice is not one to be light-
ly made.

Of one thing, however, we can be sure. There
must seldom be much point in doing the same
work for a longer period. For a student of
Chinese history, who has spent ten years in
learning the language, there is good reason to
welcome another decade spent on the actual
history. Can the same argument apply to the
manager of a dog-racing track, to a railway
porter, to the janitor of a primary school? Could
any one of these want another twenty years in
the same treadmill? Any reader who wants an
extended inning should decide, in advance, how
to spend it; and this should normally mean
something different. What is our new career to
be? If the answer is at once obvious to the
reader he may well be the sort of person whose
life should and can be prolonged. But what if
you are undecided, doubtful and hesitating? It
is a question then whether a longer life would be
of much use to you. There is no point in moving
to another and equally dull appointment. But is
there any more point in another twenty years of
gardening or golf? These are serious questions
which the individual must answer for himself.
The effort of living longer — and effort will be
required — would hardly be justified by your
solving another thousand crossword puzzles or

watching another six thousand television programmes. To make additional life acceptable to
any large number of people, we should have to
transform life itself, and no plan for this is even
under discussion.

We began with the premise that all
civilisations decline, ours being no exception.
The signs of decay are all too visible, and we
have to decide what, if anything, can be done to
halt the process or at least postpone the collapse. The remedy we suggest is to lengthen the
individual's life and so combine the energy of
youth with the wisdom of age. This brings us to
the Law of Longer Life, which reads as follows:

> *Death forms a vacuum into which we
> are drawn because we have been made to
> feel superfluous, but there may be another
> way open to us to prolong life if we choose
> to take it.*
>
> *To follow that way we need to change
> our ideas, our habits and our diet.*

Our present proposal is to extend human life by
another twenty years. There is no reason to
suppose that this will represent the final limit,
but it presents, in itself, a change that is quite
drastic enough. We are almost daunted by all
the consequential adjustments that this one
change must involve. So far the Law of Life has
been well understood as applied both to individuals and to civilisation. All must have a

birth and immaturity, a rise to a peak of achievement, a decline, a decay and death. From this sequence there has so far been no escape. We think now that a path of escape can be glimpsed, and we believe that an extension of the individual's period of achievement might at once enrich our civilisation and postpone its final and perhaps inevitable collapse. We are not certain that all we propose is possible. We do not know that the results would be exactly those we describe. We admit that there may be other results which we do not at present foresee. As against that, we have reached a position in which we have this one card left to play. We should do well to play it rather than give up the game.

APPENDIX
Swedish Exercises

Perform exercises on a daily basis, if possible, but at least three or four times per week. Maintain a comfortable pace avoiding spurts of strenuous activity. Other normal precautions should be taken before starting an exercise program of any intensity.

1

Sit upright on the floor, back straight, one leg stretched out in front of you. Bend the other leg over the outstretched leg so that the knee touches the floor on the other side. Repeat the exercise changing sides, and practice it without using the hand as a crutch behind the back. Good for seat, hips and waistline.

2

Lie flat on the floor with knees bent and feet wide apart. Raise the head and the upper part of the back until the fingertips of both hands touch one knee. Stay in this position counting to six. Lie back slowly and repeat the movement touching the other knee. This exercise is good for the stomach muscles.

3

Lie on your back in a resting position. Raise your knees and the lower part of your back as pictured. Relax slowly to original position and repeat the procedure. This is a very effective exercise for the lower part of the abdomen.

4

This is the same movement as in figure number three, but with the feet extended straight up in the air. Use the hands as an extra aid the first time, and gradually you will succeed in doing this exercise without using your hands.

5

Lie on your stomach. Raise knee and leg several times, the leg bent from the knee. Good for your seat and thighs.

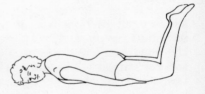

6

Same movement as in figure five, but with both legs and knees bent at the same time.

7

Stand on the knees and keep arms straight beside the body. Lean backwards from the knees. Repeat slowly. Good for the front of the thighs.

8

Stand with feet apart and somewhat turned out. Keeping both heels flat on the floor, bend the right knee and stretch as far as possible. Change sides and repeat exercise in a slow tempo. Good for a firmer hip.

9

Stand straight with your feet slightly apart and your arms extended in front of you. Bend the knees until you reach a sitting or squatting position. Count to six and then raise up. Repeat several times. Good for the thighs.